math expressions

Dr. Karen C. Fuson

Grade **K**

Volume 1

 Watch the seahorse come alive in its underwater world as you discover and solve math challenges.

Download the *Math Worlds AR* app available on Android or iOS devices.

 This material is based upon work supported by the
National Science Foundation
under Grant Numbers
ESI-9816320, REC-9806020, and RED-935373.

Any opinions, findings, and conclusions, or recommendations expressed in this material
are those of the author and do not necessarily reflect the views of the National Science Foundation.

BIG IDEA 1 - Counting and Cardinality 1–5

BIG IDEA 2 - Adding, Subtracting, and Comparing Through 5

© Houghton Mifflin Harcourt Publishing Company

BIG IDEA 1 - Partners of 5 and 6

BIG IDEA 4 - Build Teen Numbers

Student Resources

Dear Family:

Your child is learning math in an innovative program that weaves abstract mathematical concepts with the everyday experiences of children. This helps children understand math better.

Your child will have homework. He or she needs a **Homework Helper**. The helper may be anyone—you, an older brother or sister (or other family member), a neighbor, or a friend. Make a specific time for homework and provide your child with a quiet place to work (for example, no TV). Encourage your child to talk about what is happening in math class. If your child is having problems with math, please contact me to see how you might help.

Thank you! You are vital to your child's learning.

Sincerely,
Your child's teacher

- -

Please fill out the following information and return this form to the teacher.

My child _____ will have _____
                     (child's name)   (Homework Helper's name)

as his or her Homework Helper. This person is my child's

_____.
   (relationship to child: father,
   mother, sibling, friend, etc.)

Estimada familia:

Su niño está aprendiendo matemáticas con un programa innovador que relaciona conceptos matemáticos abstractos con la experiencia diaria de los niños. Esto ayuda a los niños a entender mejor las matemáticas.

Su niño tendrá tarea y necesita a una persona que lo ayude. Esa persona puede ser usted, un hermano mayor (u otro familiar), un vecino o un amigo. Establezca una hora para la tarea y ofrezca a su niño un lugar tranquilo donde trabajar (por ejemplo un lugar sin TV). Anime a su niño a comentar lo que está aprendiendo en la clase de matemáticas. Si su niño tiene problemas con las matemáticas, por favor hable con el maestro para ver cómo usted puede ayudar.

Muchas gracias. Usted es imprescindible en el aprendizaje de su niño.

Atentamente,
El maestro de su niño

- -

Por favor complete la siguiente información y devuelva este formulario al maestro.

La persona que ayudará a mi niño _____ es
(nombre del niño)

_____. Esta persona es _____
(nombre de la persona)   (relación con el niño)

de mi niño.

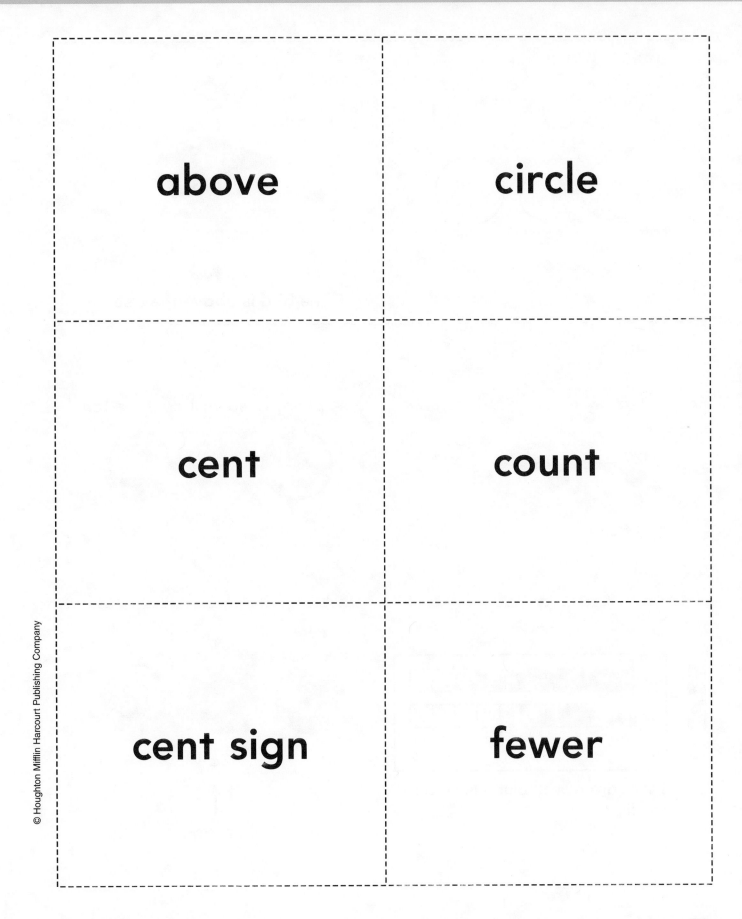

above	circle
cent	count
cent sign	fewer

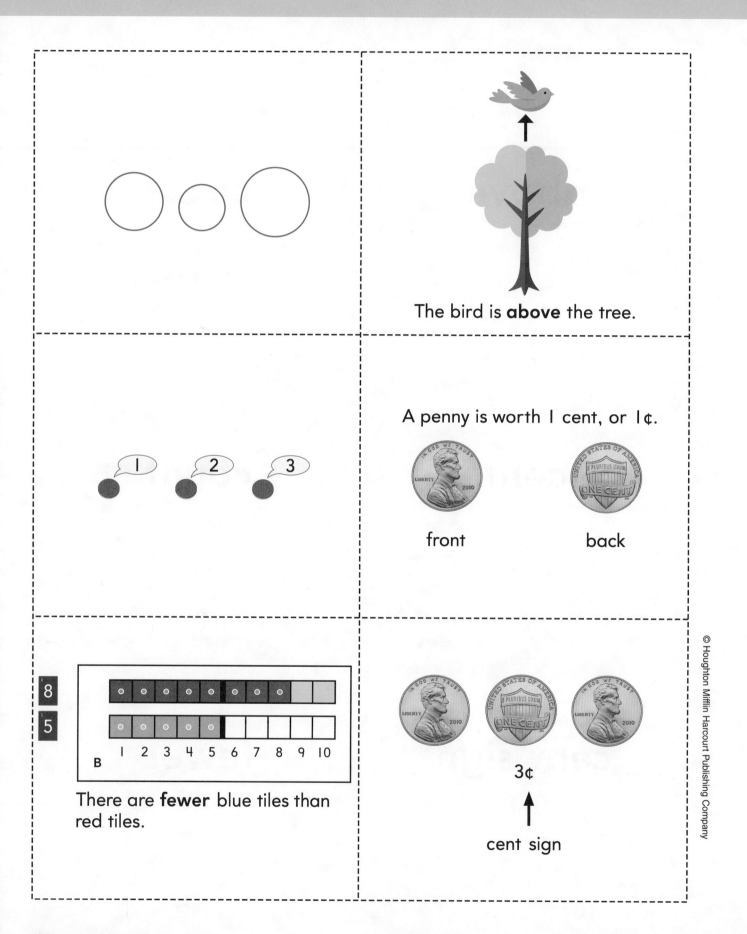

The bird is **above** the tree.

A penny is worth 1 cent, or 1¢.

front   back

8
5

There are **fewer** blue tiles than red tiles.

3¢

cent sign

five	group
four	how many
greater	in front of

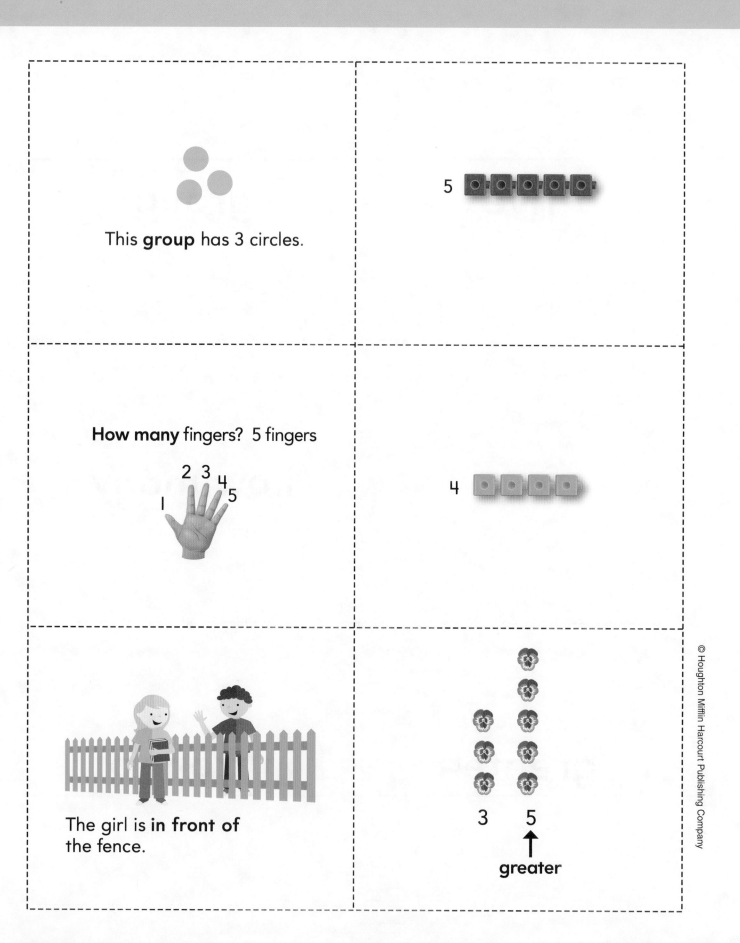

This **group** has 3 circles.

5

How many fingers? 5 fingers

2 3 4 5
1

4

The girl is **in front of** the fence.

3   5

↑
greater

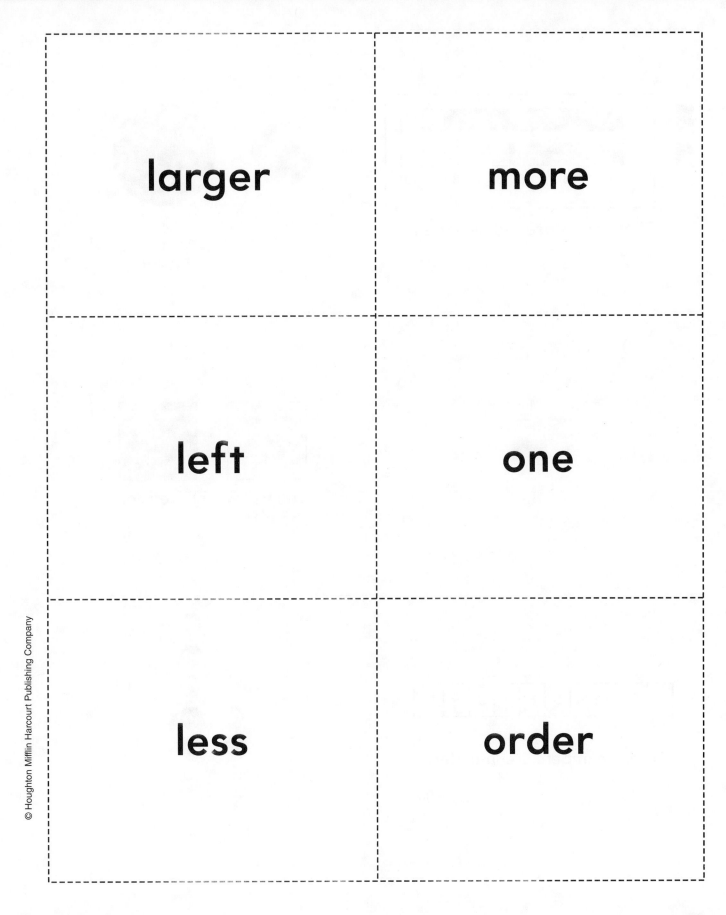

larger

more

left

one

less

order

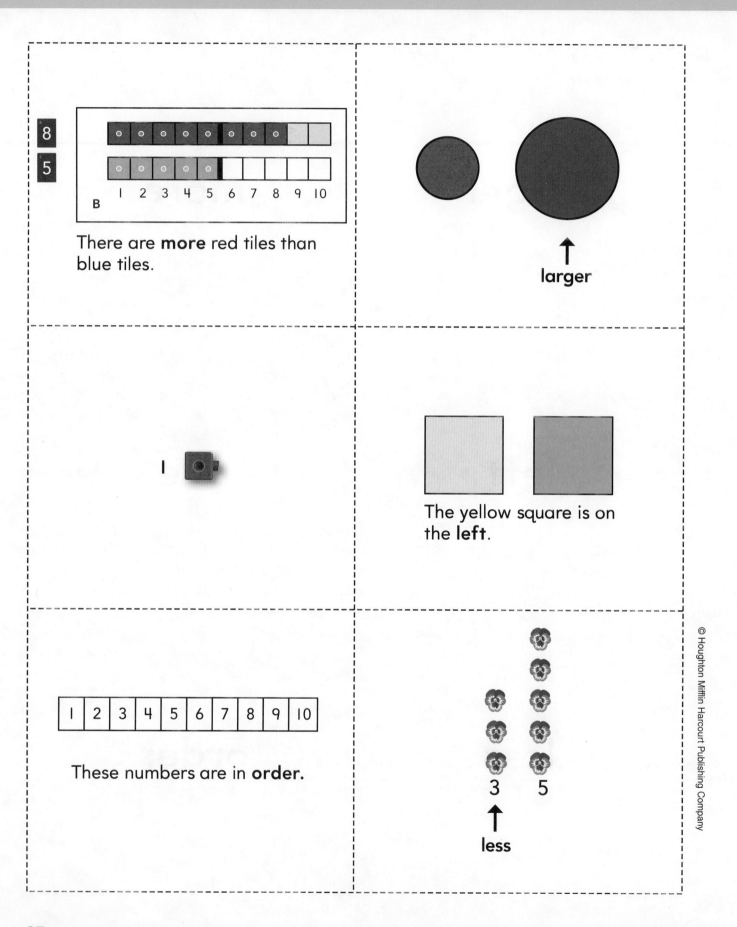

There are **more** red tiles than blue tiles.

larger

The yellow square is on the **left**.

These numbers are in **order.**

3   5

less

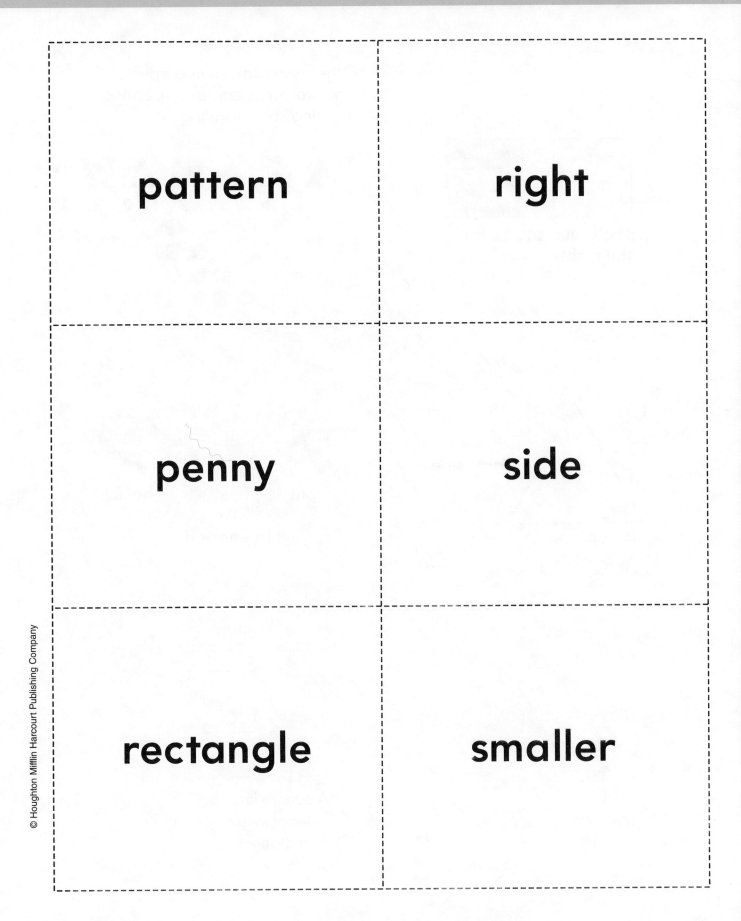

pattern

right

penny

side

rectangle

smaller

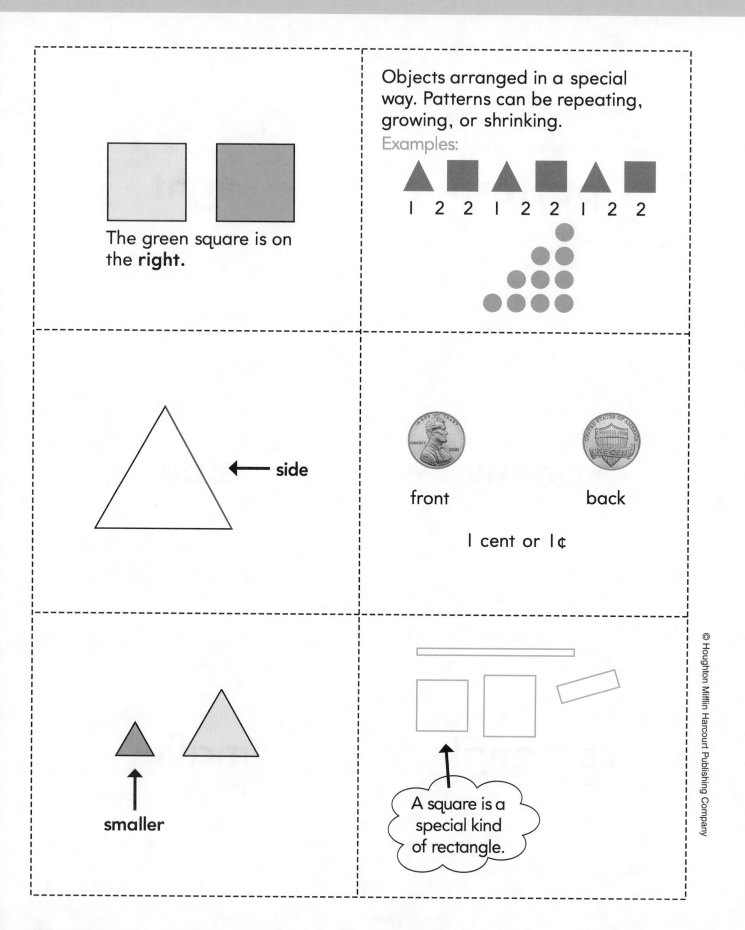

The green square is on the **right**.

Objects arranged in a special way. Patterns can be repeating, growing, or shrinking.

Examples:

1 2 2 1 2 2 1 2 2

← **side**

front   **back**

1 cent or 1¢

smaller

A square is a special kind of rectangle.

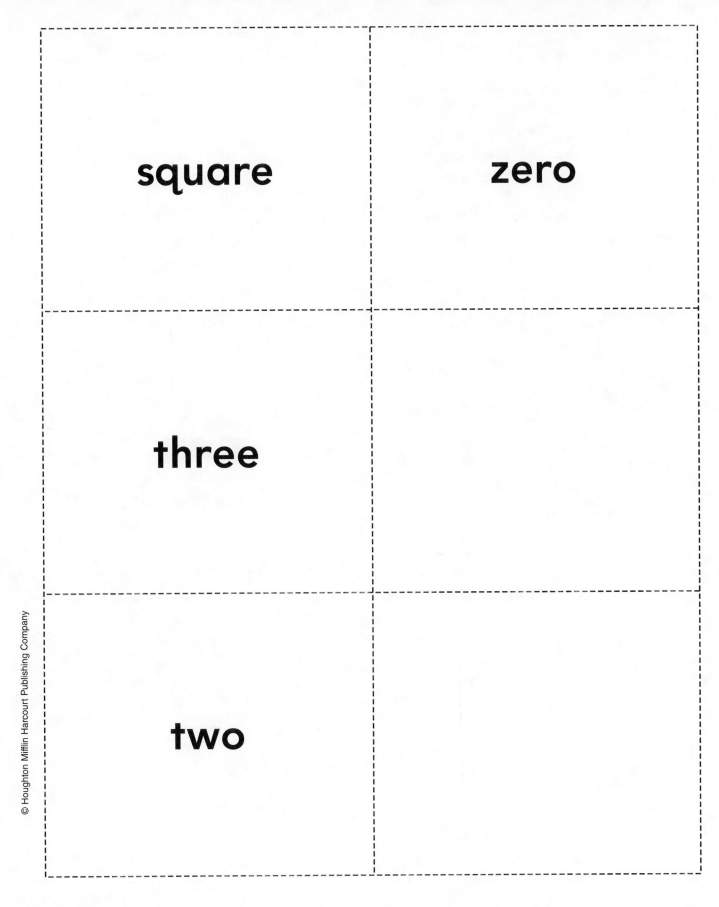

square	zero
three	
two	

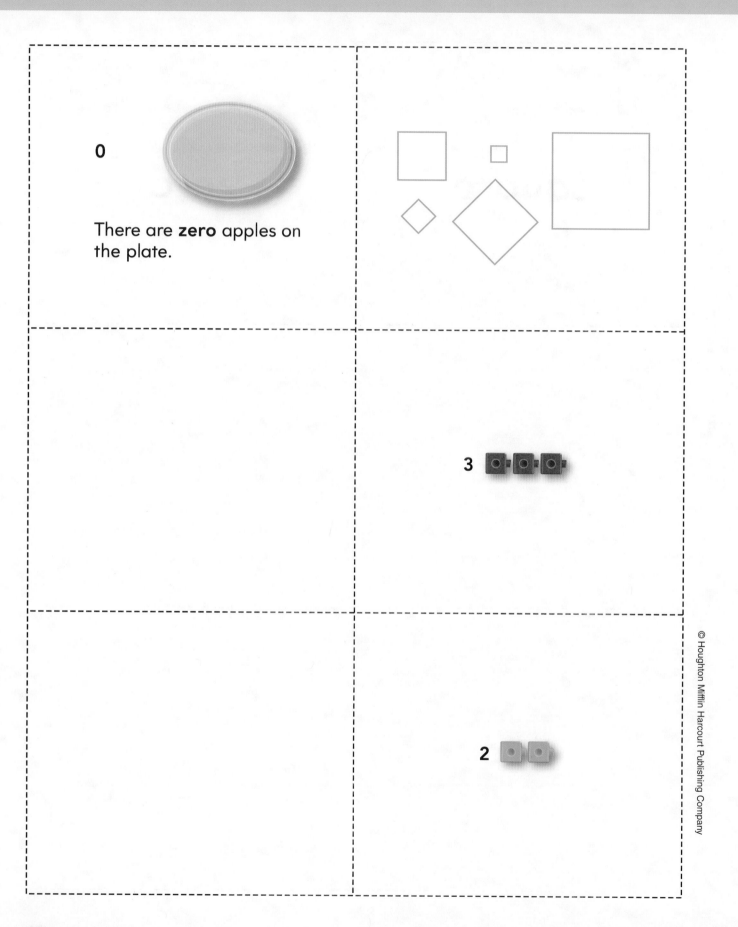

0

There are **zero** apples on the plate.

3

2

Draw a ring around 1 barn.

Draw a ring around 2 chickens.

Draw a ring around 3 cows.

Draw a ring around 2 slides.

Draw a ring around 4 swings.

Draw a ring around 5 children.

✔ Check Understanding

TEACHER: Count the number of birds and tell how many.

© Houghton Mifflin Harcourt Publishing Company

Introduce Number and Counting Routines

Number Tiles and Square-Inch Tiles **5**

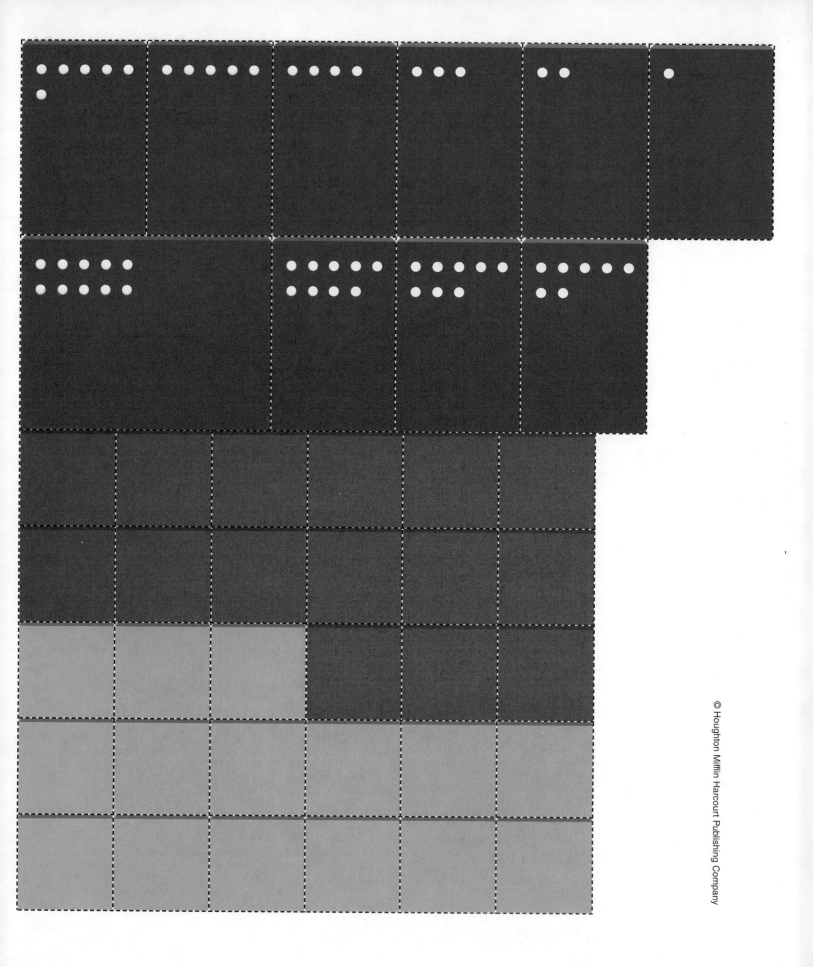

Number Tiles and Square-Inch Tiles

Name _____

Draw a line. Match the Number Tile to the same number of squares.

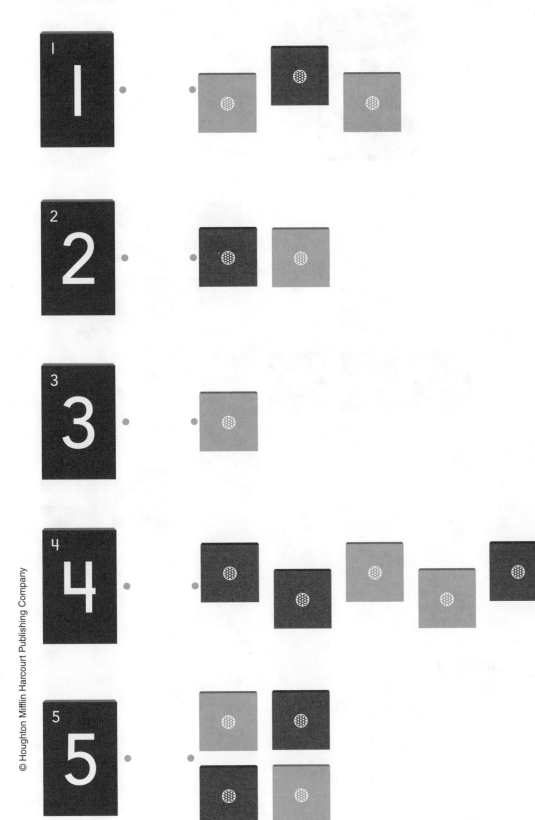

Relate Objects and Numbers Through 5 **7**

Ring the **groups** of tiles that match the Number Tile.

VOCABULARY
groups

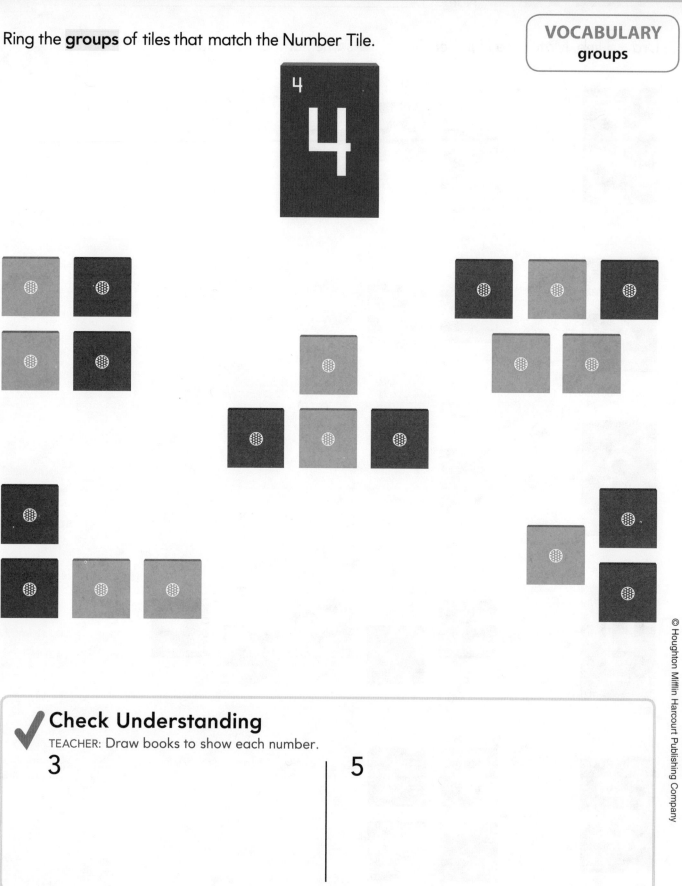

✔ Check Understanding

TEACHER: Draw books to show each number.

3

5

Relate Objects and Numbers Through 5

Dear Family:

Your child has just read and discussed *Anno's Counting Book*. This book is an introduction to beginning numbers. It is filled with charming scenes that show many things all of the same number (for example, a scene showing many different groups of 3 things). Each page shows a month of the year.

We have discussed what a scene is in class. *A scene is a place where some action or event occurs, a picture*. The children will be making their own scenes or pictures. Sometimes this will be started in class and completed for homework. You can help by talking with your child about what he or she might draw, for example, your child might draw 2 of something, such as things found in a kitchen—2 plates, 2 bowls, 2 spoons.

Help your child practice counting things in daily life. Children might count how many stairs there are in your home, how many plates you need to set the table, or how many people are in the family.

Thank you for helping your child learn more about numbers and counting!

Sincerely,
Your child's teacher

Estimada familia:

Su niño acaba de leer y comentar un libro para contar. Este libro es una introducción a los primeros números. Está lleno de escenas fascinantes que muestran muchas cosas, todas acerca de los mismos números (por ejemplo, una escena muestra varios grupos diferentes de 3 cosas). Cada página indica un mes del año.

Hemos comentado en clase lo que es una escena. *Una escena es un lugar donde ocurre una acción o un suceso, un dibujo.* Los niños van a hacer sus propias escenas o dibujos. A veces los empezarán en clase y los terminarán de tarea. Usted puede ayudar hablando con su niño sobre lo que puede dibujar. Por ejemplo: si va a dibujar 2 de algo, podría dibujar cosas que están en la cocina, 2 platos, 2 tazones, 2 cucharas.

Ayude a su niño a practicar contando cosas que usen a diario. Los niños pueden contar cuántas escaleras hay en su casa, cuántos platos se necesitan para poner la mesa o cuántas personas hay en la familia.

¡Gracias por ayudar a su niño a aprender más sobre los números y a contar!

Atentamente,
El maestro de su niño

Draw Scenes of 2 and 3

Name _____

Draw a scene with groups of 2.

Draw a scene with groups of 3.

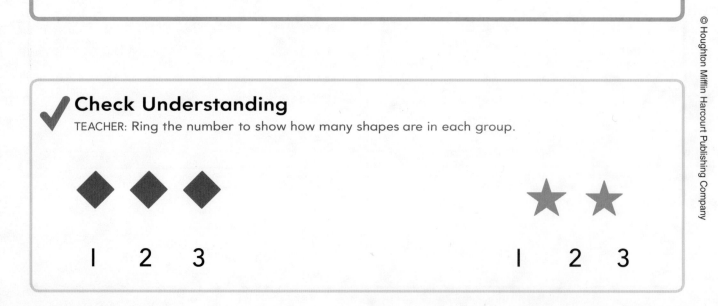

✓ Check Understanding

TEACHER: Ring the number to show how many shapes are in each group.

1   2   3   1   2   3

          Draw Scenes of 2 and 3

Find groups of 3.

Color the objects that are in groups of 3.

Find groups of 2.

Color the objects that are in groups of 2.

✔ Check Understanding

TEACHER: Place 3 Square-Inch tiles in a row as shown. Now move the tiles so the group looks different. Draw to show what the new group looks like.

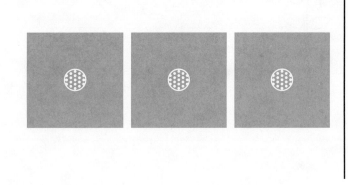

Counting and Cardinality 1–5

Draw a scene with groups of 4.

Draw a scene with groups of 5.

Check Understanding

TEACHER: Draw 4 apples. Draw 4 oranges. Count the apples. Tell how many. Count the oranges. Tell how many.

| 4 apples | 4 oranges |

Counting and Cardinality Through 5

Name _____

Look at the picture.
How many cats are there?

Look at what Puzzled Penguin wrote.
Help Puzzled Penguin.

I cat

Am I correct?

Count the cats.
Ring the number of cats.

0   2

Count the dogs.
Ring the number of dogs.

3   5

Draw 5 hats.

Draw 3 cats.

Draw 4 stars.

Draw 2 cars.

✔ Check Understanding

TEACHER: Count the balls. Ring the number.

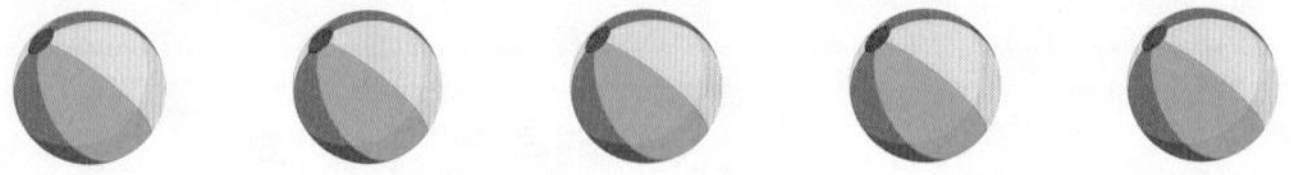

3   4   5

Scenes and Visual Imagery

VOCABULARY
how many

Put out 1 red square.

Put out 2 blue squares.

Draw to show **how many** squares in all.

Put out 2 red squares.

Put out 2 blue squares.

Draw to show how many squares in all.

Put out 5 red squares.

Take away 2 squares.

Draw to show how many squares are left.

_____

Put out 4 red squares.

Take away 3 squares.

Draw to show how many squares are left.

✔ **Check Understanding**

TEACHER: Clap to show how many red squares. Clap to show how many blue squares. How many squares are there in all?

Introduce Adding and Subtracting

Circles

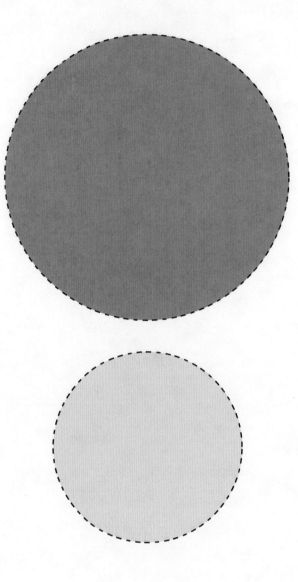

Circles

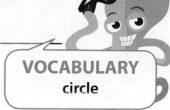

VOCABULARY
circle

Trace each **circle**.
Color the circles.

Look at the red circle.

Draw two circles that are **larger**.

Draw two circles that are **smaller**.

Color the circles different colors.

VOCABULARY
larger
smaller

✔ **Check Understanding**

TEACHER: Choose 2 of the circles you drew above. How are they alike? How are they different?

Identify Circles

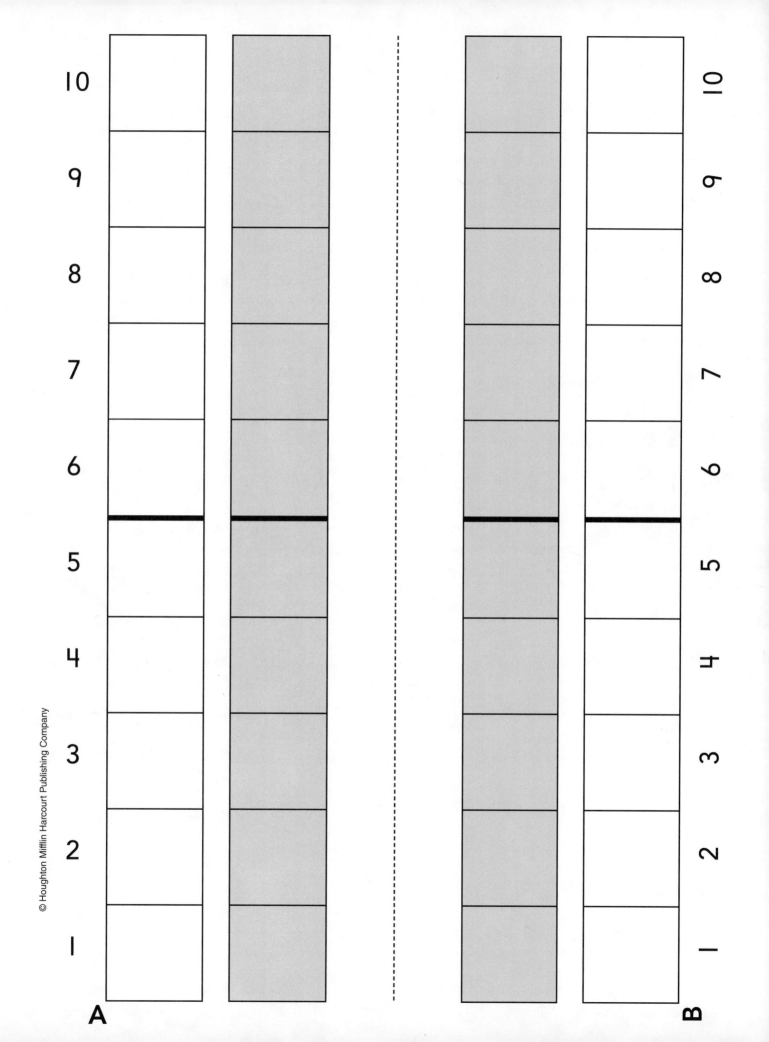

Comparing Mat

Name _____

VOCABULARY
less
greater

Look at the comparing mat.

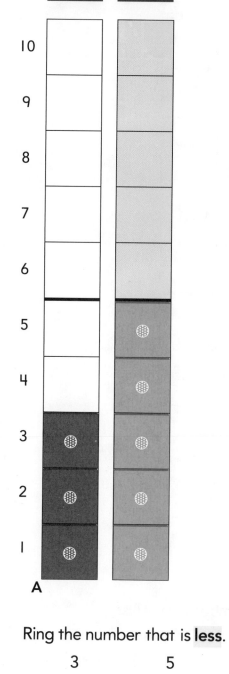

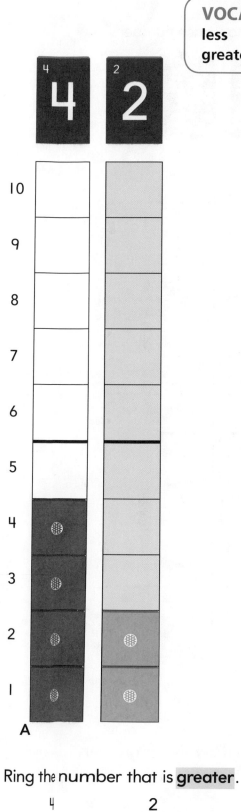

Ring the number that is **less**.

3   5

Ring the number that is **greater**.

4   2

Color to show each number.

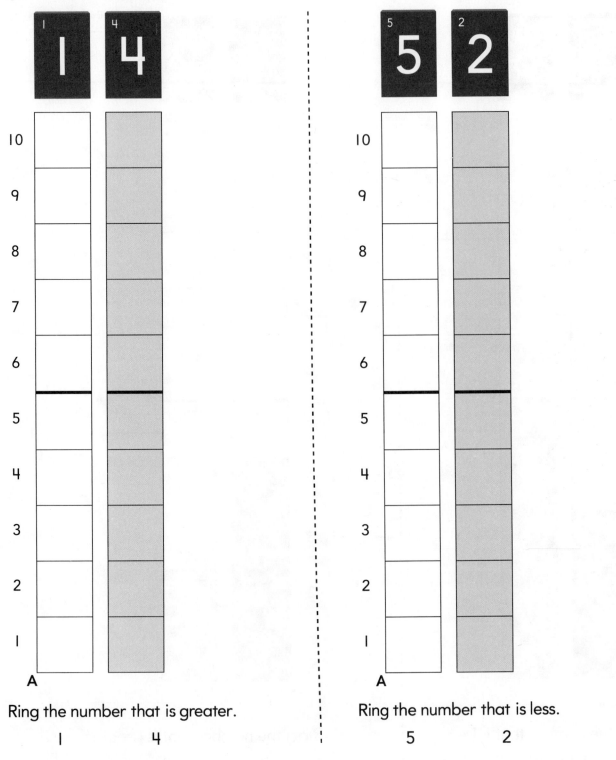

Ring the number that is greater.

    1   4

Ring the number that is less.

    5   2

✔ Check Understanding

TEACHER: Use Comparing Mat B. Put 3 tiles on the top row and 1 on the bottom row. Explain what it shows.

Introduce Comparing

Squares and Rectangles

Squares and Rectangles

VOCABULARY
square

Color each circle yellow. Color each **square** blue.
Draw a face under your favorite hat.

Color each kind of shape as shown.

VOCABULARY
rectangle

circle   square   **rectangle**

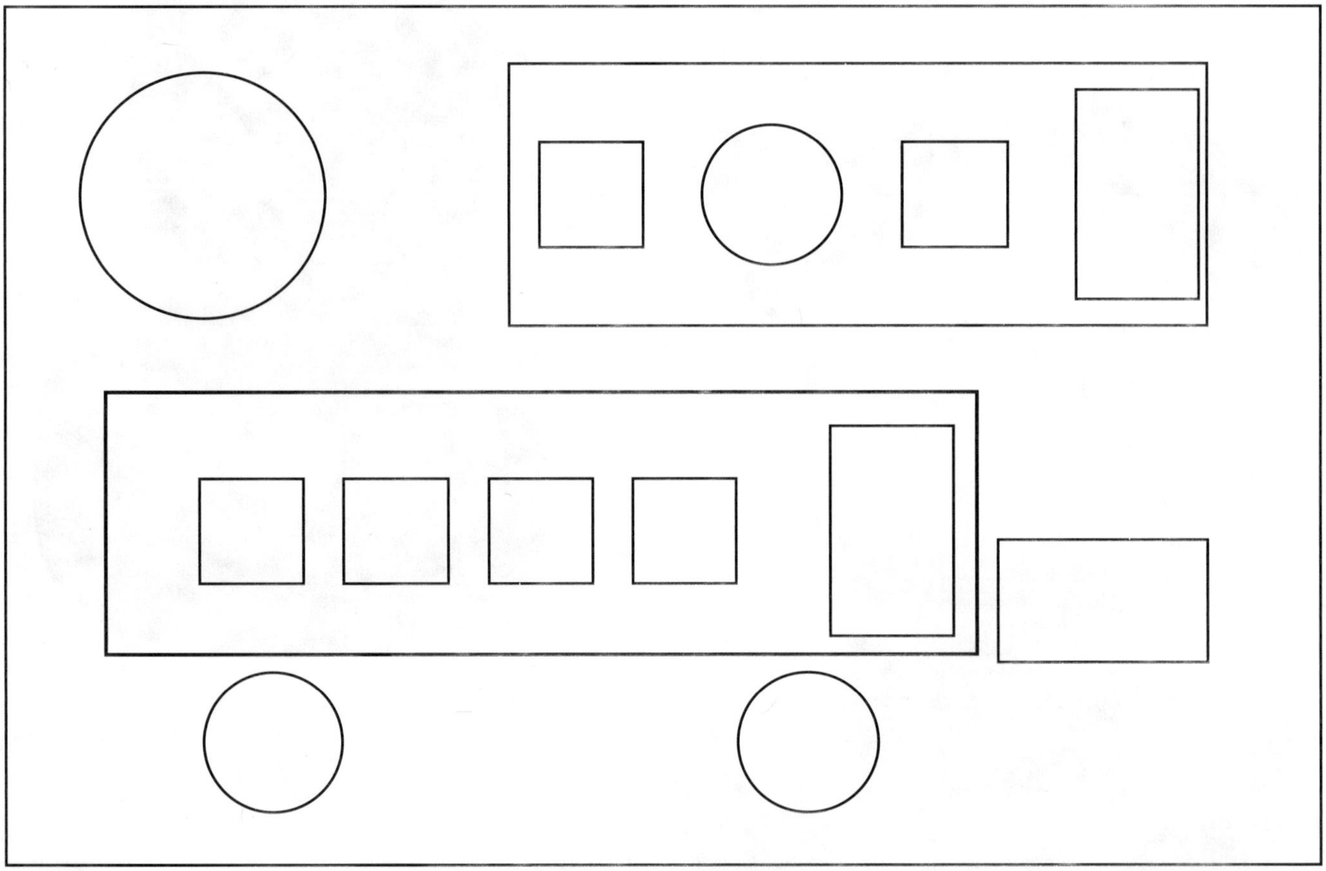

✔ Check Understanding

TEACHER: Look at the green shape. Ring the name of the shape.

circle

square

rectangle

© Houghton Mifflin Harcourt Publishing Company

Identify Squares and Rectangles

Name _____

VOCABULARY
fewer
more

Color to show each number.
Ring the tower with **fewer**.

Color to show each number.
Ring the tower with **more**.

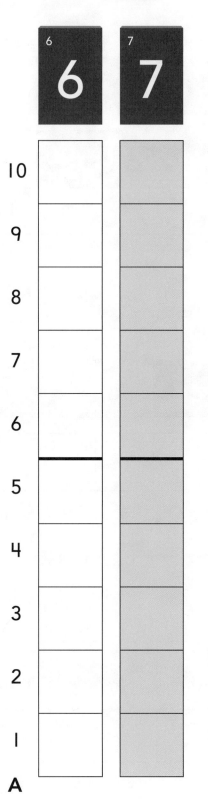

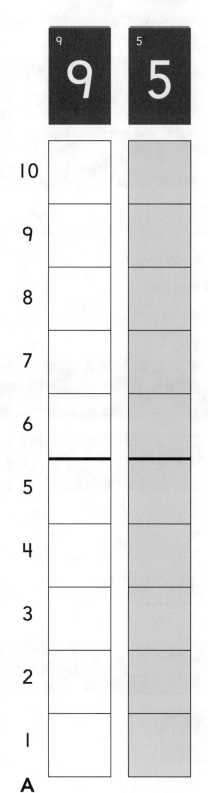

Sal says the row with 9 has more.

Jenna says the row with 8 has more.

Who is correct? Ring your answer.   Sal   Jenna

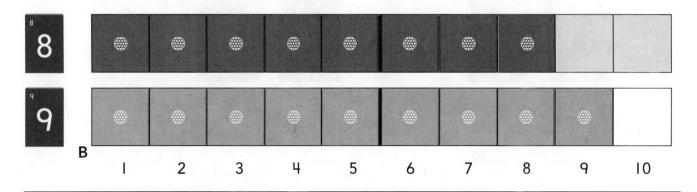

Ava says the row with 7 has fewer.

Jin says the row with 5 has fewer.

Who is correct? Ring your answer.   Ava   Jin

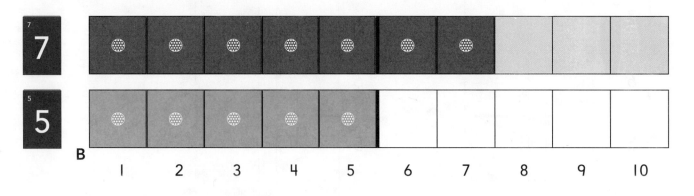

✓ Check Understanding

TEACHER: What does this picture show?

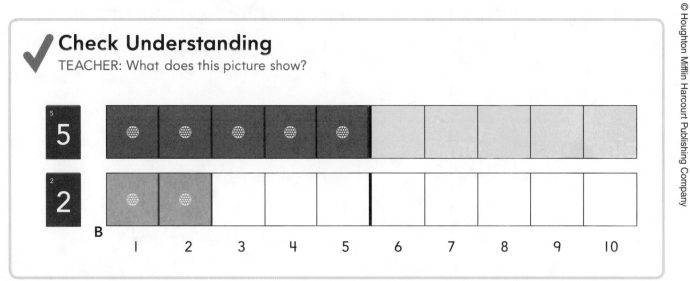

Count from 1 to 10

Dear Family:

Your child is learning to write numbers. Numbers will be written to identify how many objects are in a group and to order numbers. Your child will also write numbers to identify the value of a coin or a group of coins. You might notice that sometimes your child might write numbers backwards or reverse them. This is very common in early number writing. You can ask your child, "Does this number look OK?" Then point out that it is written backwards. Eventually our goal is that children may identify their own reversals, write correct numbers, and write faster in preparation for first grade.

In this unit, your child will also be introduced to patterns and how to analyze them. Patterns help build a solid foundation for mathematics. Point out patterns you come across throughout your everyday life. You may find patterns on fabric, on a ceiling, on a rug, on a display, or on a building.

Thank you!

Sincerely,
Your child's teacher

Estimada familia:

Su niño está aprendiendo a escribir los números. Los números se escribirán para identificar cuántos objetos hay en un grupo y para ordenar números. Su niño también escribirá números para identificar el valor de una moneda o un grupo de monedas. Usted observará que a veces su niño escribe los números al revés o que los invierte. Esto es normal al empezar a escribir los números. Puede preguntarle, "¿Está bien escrito este número?" Luego indíquele que está escrito al revés. Nuestro objetivo es que, más adelante, los niños se den cuenta de que han invertido los números, que los escriban correctamente y que escriban más rápido para prepararse para el primer grado.

En esta unidad, a su niño también se le presentarán patrones y cómo analizarlos. Los patrones ayudan a establecer una buena base para las matemáticas. Señale patrones que ven en su vida cotidiana. Pueden hallar patrones en tela, en un techo, en una alfombra, en una exhibición o en un edificio.

¡Gracias!

Atentamente,
El maestro de su niño

Name _____

Write the numbers.

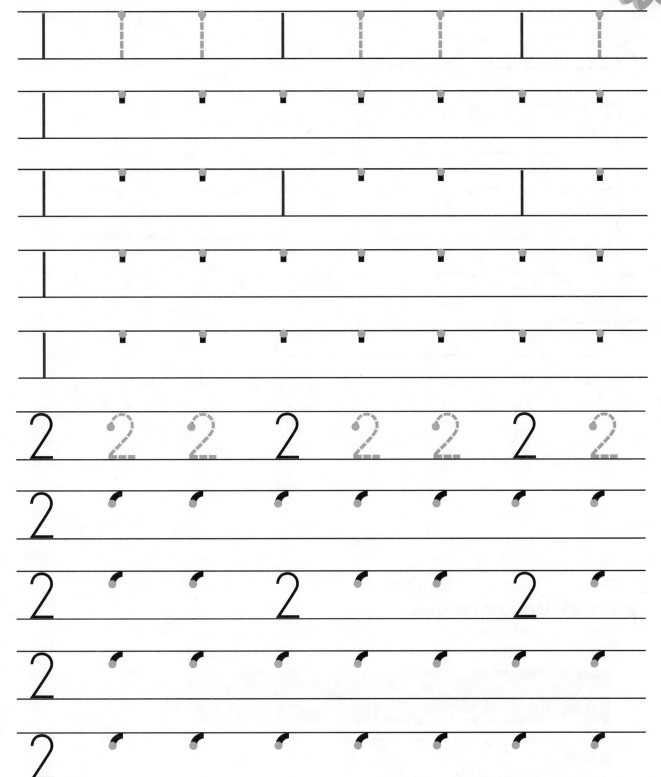

Write the number 3.

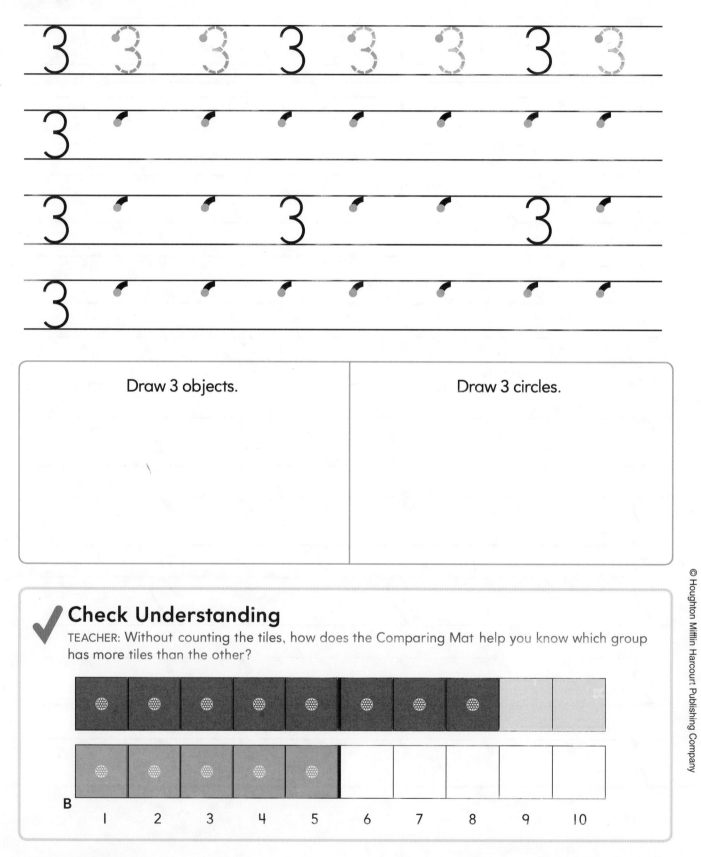

3 3 3 3 3 3 3 3

3

3   3   3

3

Draw 3 objects.	Draw 3 circles.

✔ **Check Understanding**

TEACHER: Without counting the tiles, how does the Comparing Mat help you know which group has more tiles than the other?

B
1   2   3   4   5   6   7   8   9   10

© Houghton Mifflin Harcourt Publishing Company

Name ______________________________

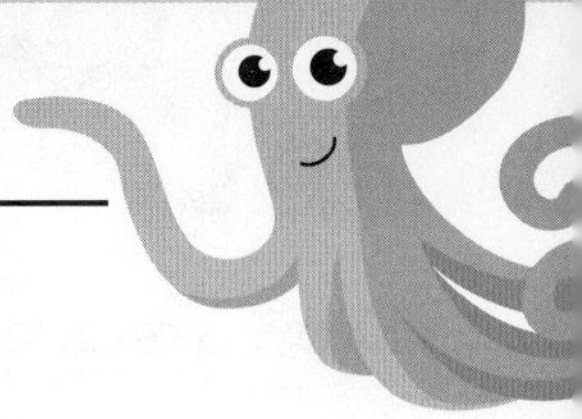

Go left to right.

Ring groups of the number.

Mark an X on the groups that are not the number.

3

4 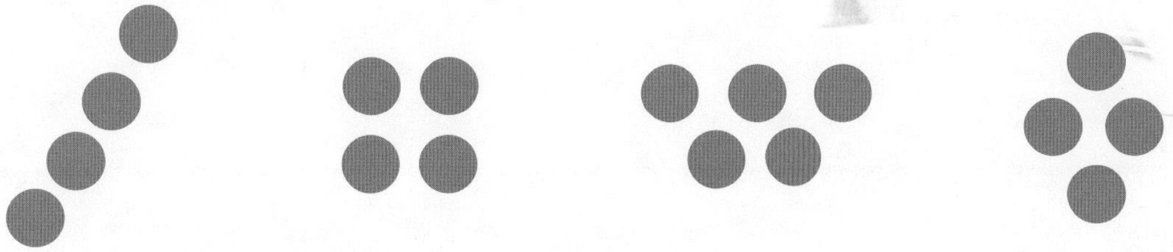

5 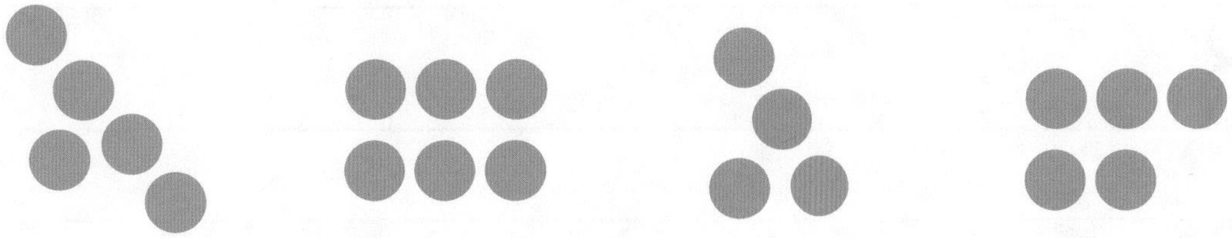

2 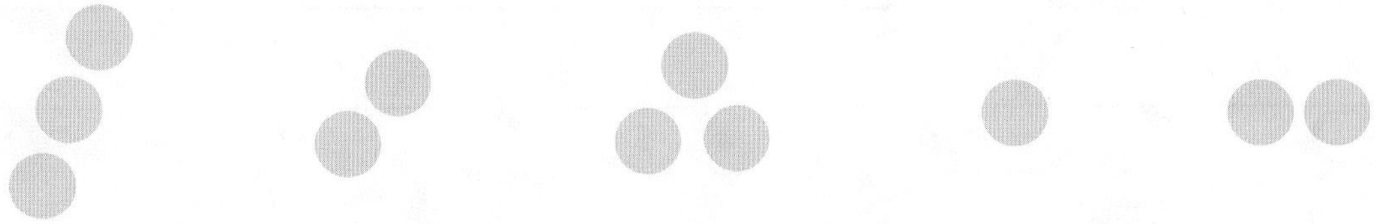

Draw 3 rectangles.

Write the number 3.

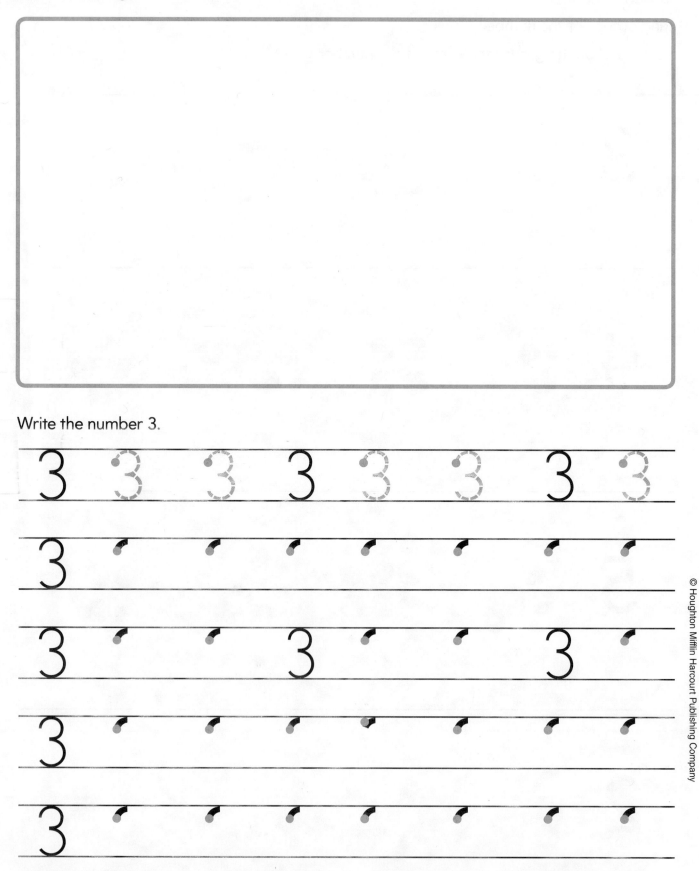

Practice Numbers 1–10

Name _____

A **penny** is worth I **cent**, or I¢.

The **cent sign (¢)** shows the number of cents.

VOCABULARY
penny
cent
cent sign (¢)

Count the pennies.
Ring the number of cents.

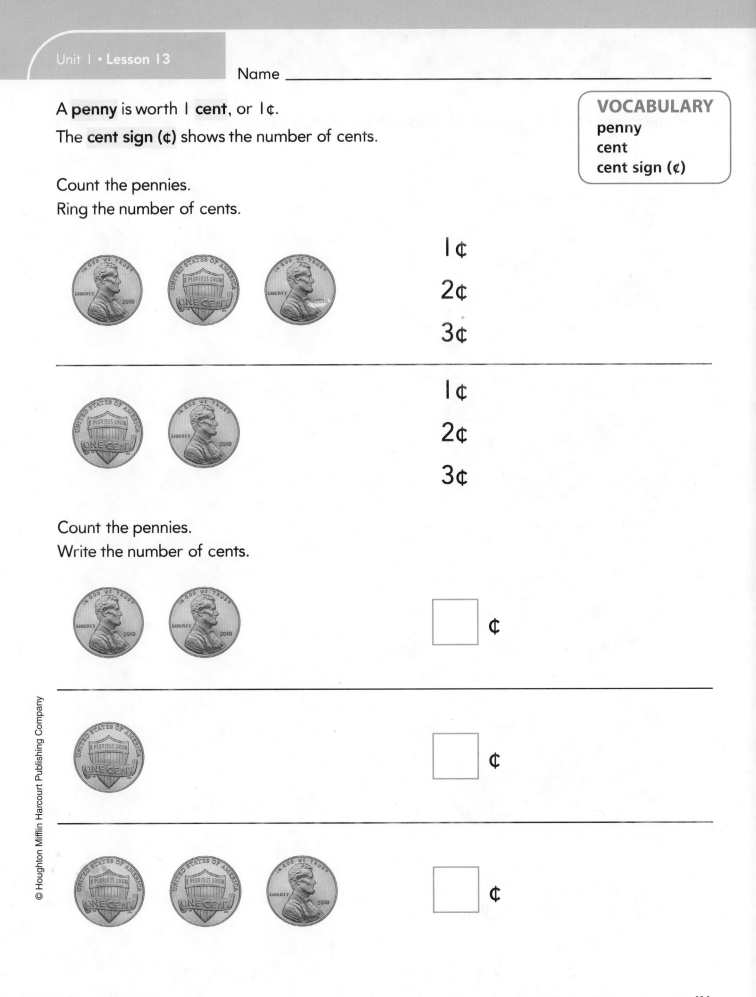

I¢
2¢
3¢

I¢
2¢
3¢

Count the pennies.
Write the number of cents.

☐ ¢

☐ ¢

☐ ¢

Draw lines to match each group of pennies with the number of cents.

   •   • 2¢

   •   • 3¢

   •   • 4¢

   •   • 5¢

✓ **Check Understanding**

TEACHER: Draw 3 apples. Then draw 3 apples another way.

Practice Numbers 1–10

Name _____

Write the number 4.

4 4 4 4 4 4 4

4

4 4 4

4

4

Draw 4 objects.	Draw 4 rectangles.

Numbers of Objects in a Group **43**

Trace the number 4. Color each group of 4 a different color.
Mark an X on the objects that are not in a group of 4.

Numbers of Objects in a Group

Name _____

Tell an adding story.

First	Then	At the end

Tell a subtracting story.

First	Then	At the end

Numbers of Objects in a Group **45**

Tell math stories about the pictures.

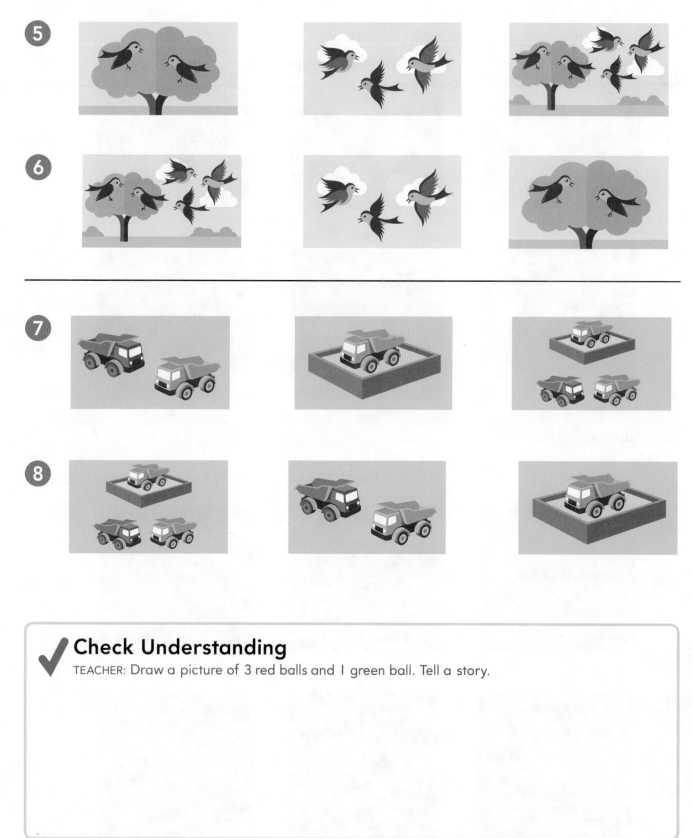

5

6

7

8

✔ Check Understanding

TEACHER: Draw a picture of 3 red balls and 1 green ball. Tell a story.

Numbers of Objects in a Group

Name _____

Puzzled Penguin compared numbers.

Puzzled Penguin showed the numbers.

Then Puzzled Penguin drew a ring around
the number that is greater. Help Puzzled Penguin.

Am I correct?

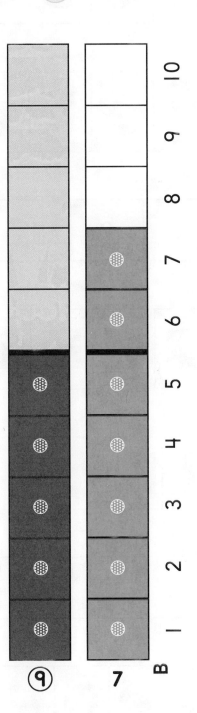

A ⑥   8

⑨   7   B

Ring the part of the **pattern** that repeats.

VOCABULARY
pattern

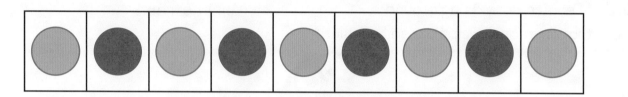

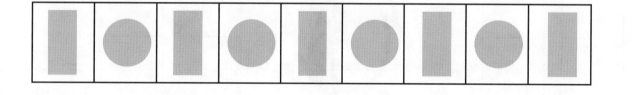

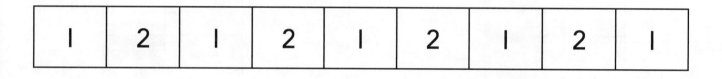

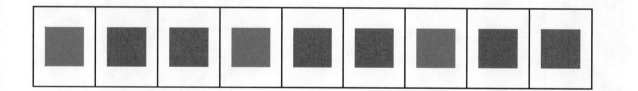

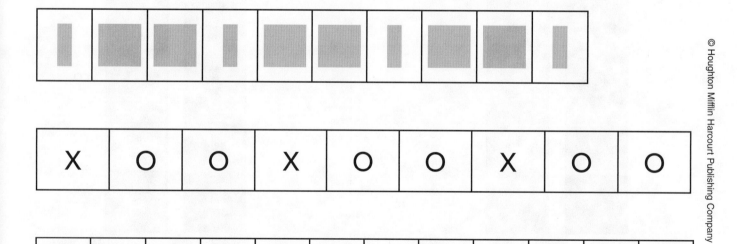

Objects and Numbers Through 10

Name _____

Draw to continue the pattern.

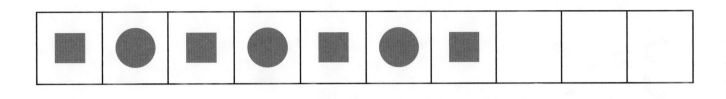

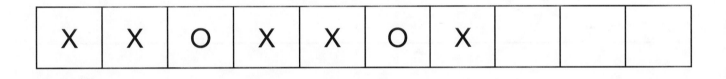

| X | X | O | X | X | O | X | | | |

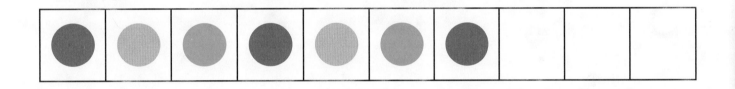

| 1 | 2 | 2 | 1 | 2 | 2 | 1 | | | |

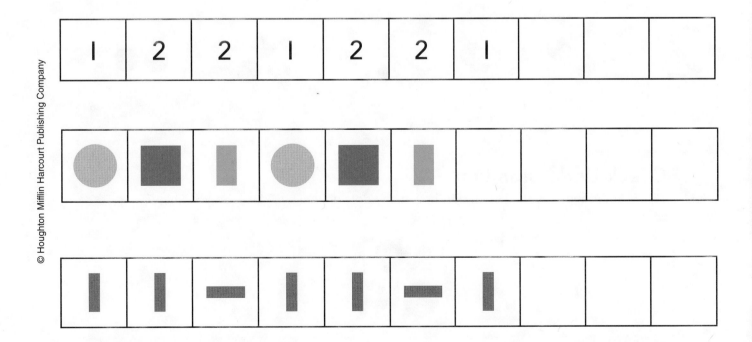

Go left to right. Ring groups of the number. Mark an X on the groups that are not the number.

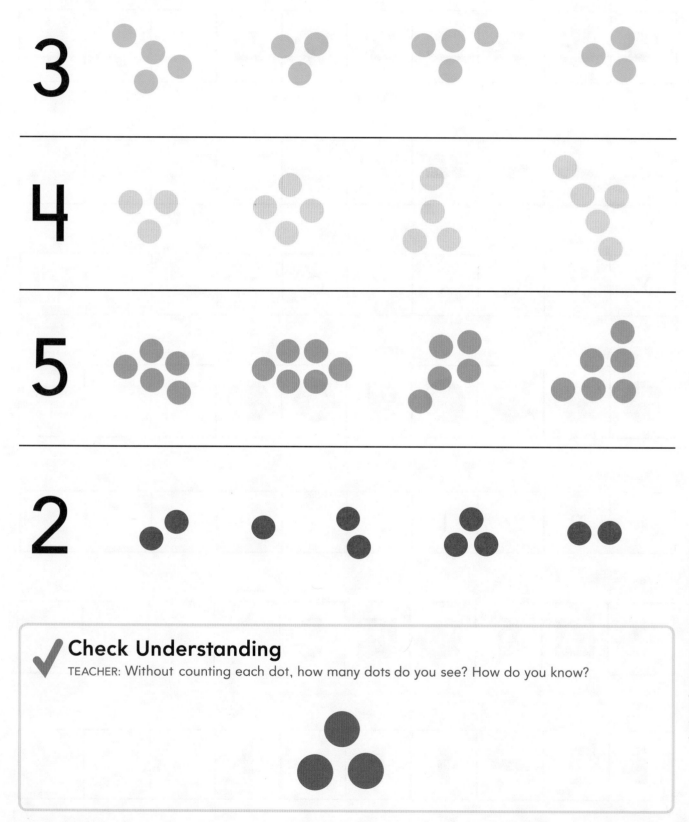

✔ **Check Understanding**

TEACHER: Without counting each dot, how many dots do you see? How do you know?

Objects and Numbers Through 10

Name _____

Write the number 5.

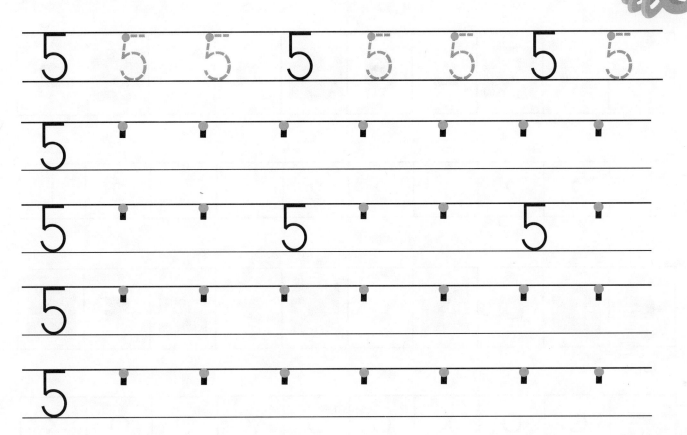

Draw 5 objects.	Draw 5 squares.

Practice: Number of Objects in a Group **51**

Draw to complete the pattern.

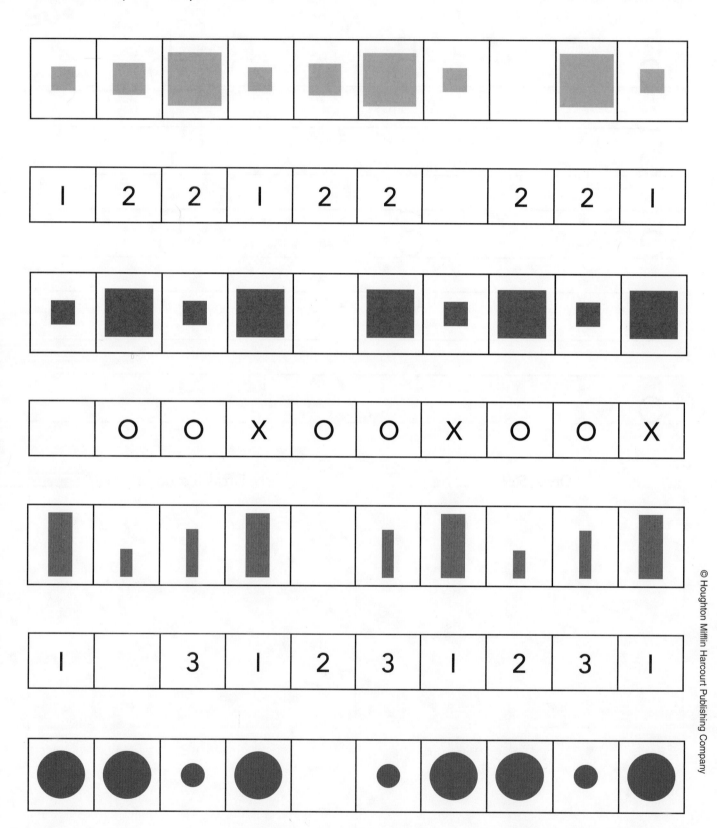

Practice: Number of Objects in a Group

Rectangles and Squares **53**

Rectangles and Squares

Name _____

Draw two different AB patterns.
Use numbers for one and shapes for the other.

A	B	A	B	A	B	A	B	A	B

Draw two different ABB patterns.
Use numbers for one and shapes for the other.

A	B	B	A	B	B	A	B	B	A

Draw two different ABC patterns.
Use numbers for one and shapes for the other.

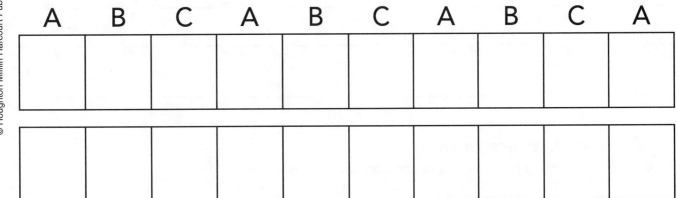

A	B	C	A	B	C	A	B	C	A

Count the animals. Ring the number. Then color each group a different color.

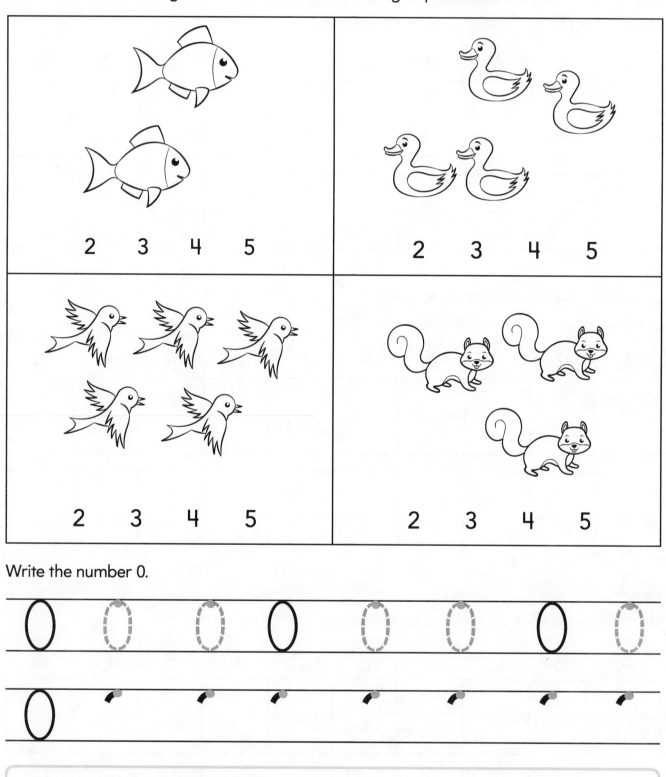

2   3   4   5

2   3   4   5

2   3   4   5

2   3   4   5

Write the number 0.

© Houghton Mifflin Harcourt Publishing Company

✓ Check Understanding

TEACHER: Draw a group of 4 dots. Draw another group with fewer dots.

Practice: Number of Objects in a Group

Connect the dots in **order**.

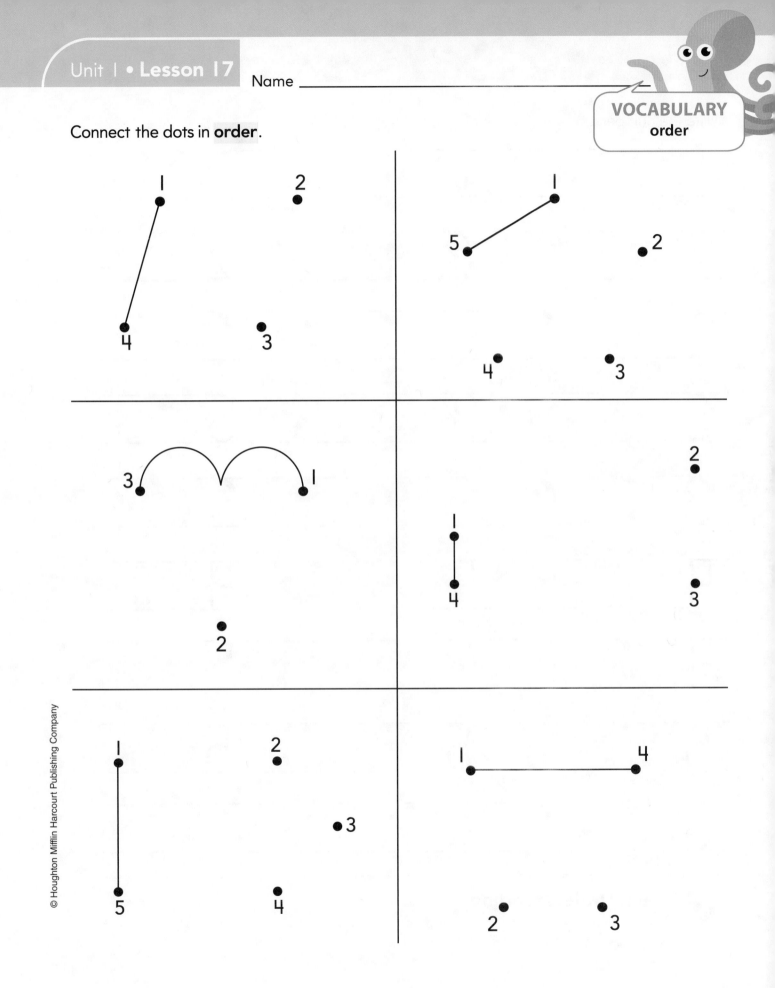

More Objects and Numbers Through 10 **57**

Write the numbers.

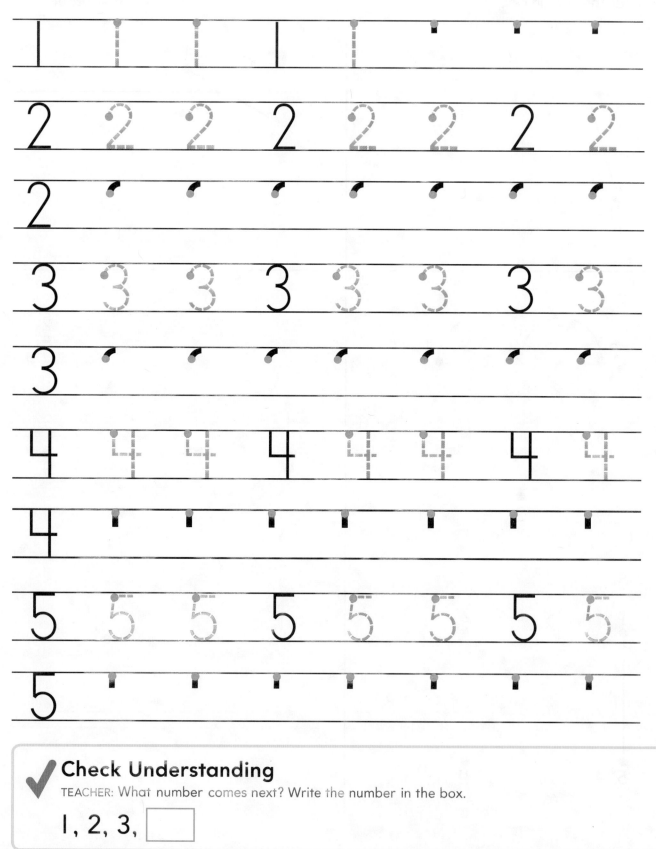

✔ Check Understanding

TEACHER: What number comes next? Write the number in the box.

1, 2, 3, ☐

More Objects and Numbers Through 10

VOCABULARY
sides

Color shapes with 0 straight **sides** blue.
Color shapes with 4 sides red.

Draw some more shapes with 0 straight sides.
Draw some more shapes with 4 sides.

Focus on Problem Solving

Name ______________________ Date ____________

Ring groups of the number. Mark an X on the groups that are not the number.

1

4 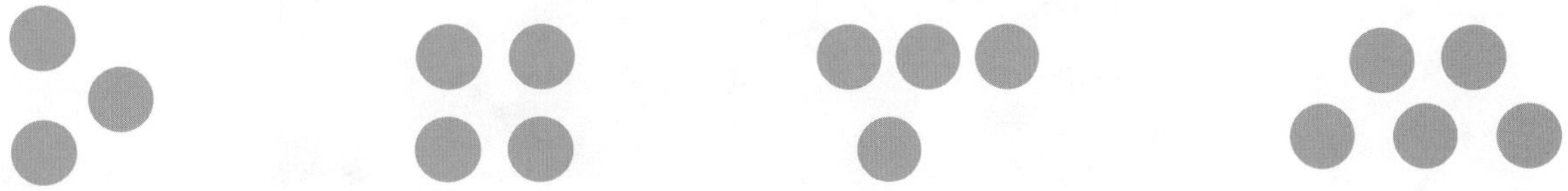

2

2

3 Draw 3 trees.	**4** Draw 5 flowers.

5 Count the pennies.
Write the number of cents.

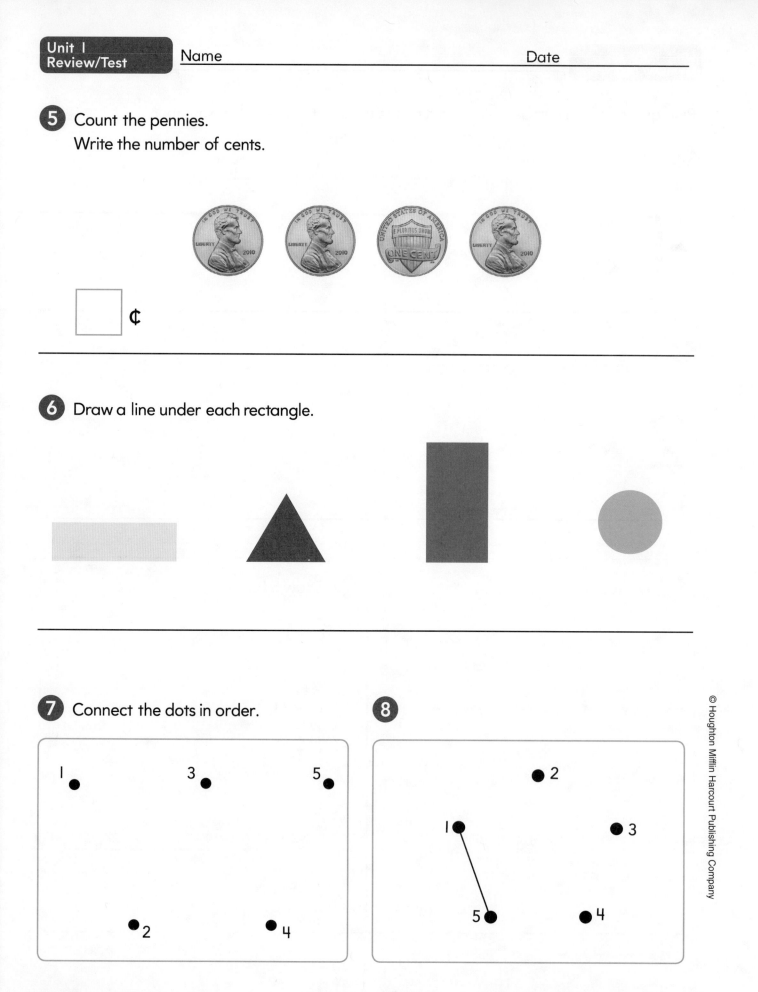

▢ ¢

---

6 Draw a line under each rectangle.

---

7 Connect the dots in order.

1 •   3 •   5 •

•2   •4

8

•2

1 •   •3

5 •   •4

© Houghton Mifflin Harcourt Publishing Company

9 Write the numbers.

10 Does the picture match the number? Choose Yes or No.

3   ○ Yes   ○ No

11 Use shapes to draw a repeating pattern.
Ring the part of the pattern that repeats.
How many of each shape did you draw?

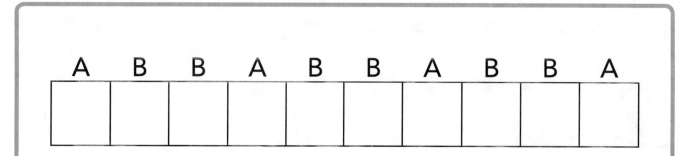

A	B	B	A	B	B	A	B	B	A

☐ shapes

Number Train

Part A

Part B

Dear Family:

Children are learning to see numbers 6, 7, 8, 9, and 10 as having a 5 and some more. This is called using a 5-group. This visual pattern will help children add, subtract, and understand numbers. It will also help later in multidigit calculation.

Count things at home in 5-groups to help your child see the 5 in 6, 7, 8, 9, and 10. For example, 7 buttons can be counted using 5-groups: "5 and 2 make 7."

Children will see 5-groups in materials they are using in school:

Number Parade

Square-Inch Tiles

Counters and 5-Counter Strips

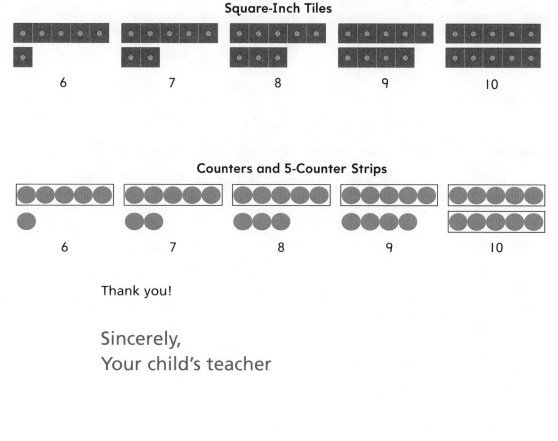

Thank you!

Sincerely,
Your child's teacher

Estimada familia:

Los niños están aprendiendo a ver que los números 6, 7, 8, 9 y 10 contienen el 5 y algo más. Esto se llama usar un grupo de 5. Este patrón visual los ayudará a sumar, a restar y a entender los números. Más adelante también les servirá para los cálculos con números de más de un dígito.

Cuenten cosas en casa haciendo grupos de 5 para que el niño identifique el 5 en el 6, 7, 8, 9 y 10. Por ejemplo, pueden contar 7 botones haciendo un grupo de 5: "5 más 2 son 7".

Los niños identificarán grupos de 5 en los materiales que usan en la escuela:

Desfile de números

Azulejos de una pulgada cuadrada

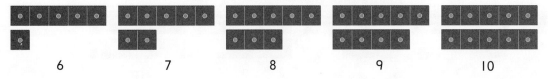

6   7   8   9   10

Fichas y tiras de 5 fichas

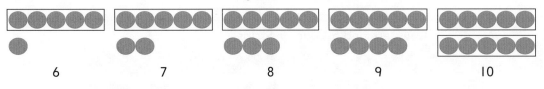

6   7   8   9   10

¡Muchas gracias!

Atentamente,
El maestro de su niño

Find Numbers 1–10: Neighborhood Scene

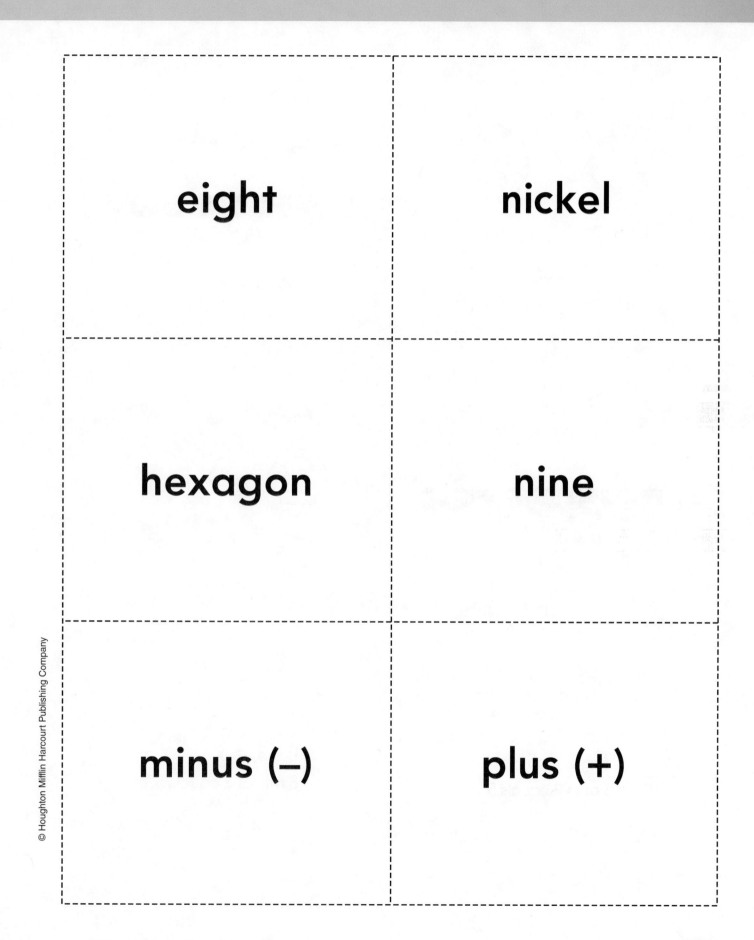

eight

nickel

hexagon

nine

minus (–)

plus (+)

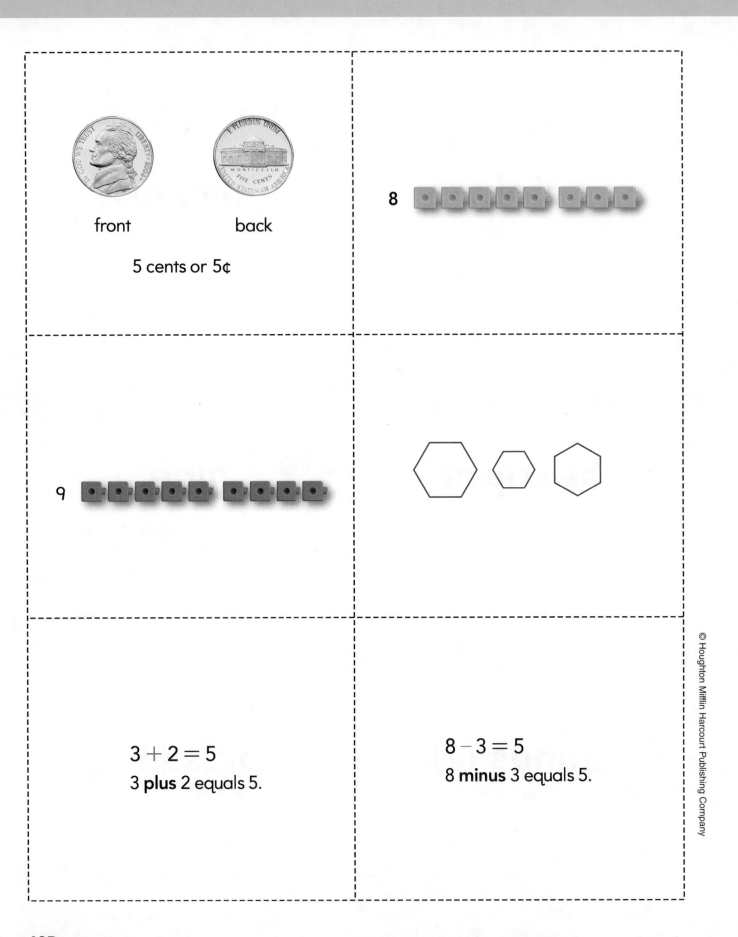

front   back

5 cents or 5¢

8

9

3 + 2 = 5
3 **plus** 2 equals 5.

8 − 3 = 5
8 **minus** 3 equals 5.

© Houghton Mifflin Harcourt Publishing Company

seven	ten
six	triangle
straight lines	

10

7

6

Straight lines do not curve.

Cut on dashed lines.
Do not cut on solid lines.

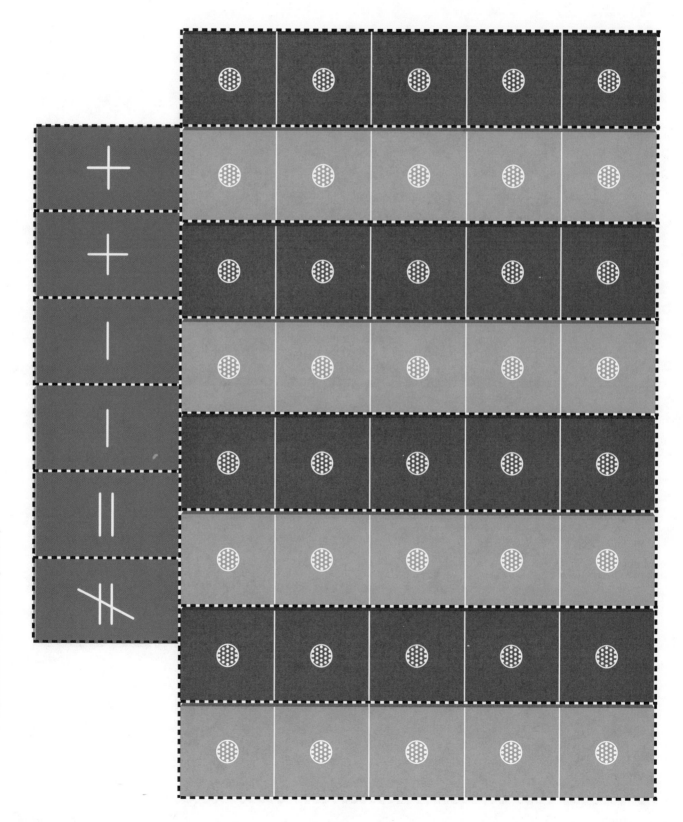

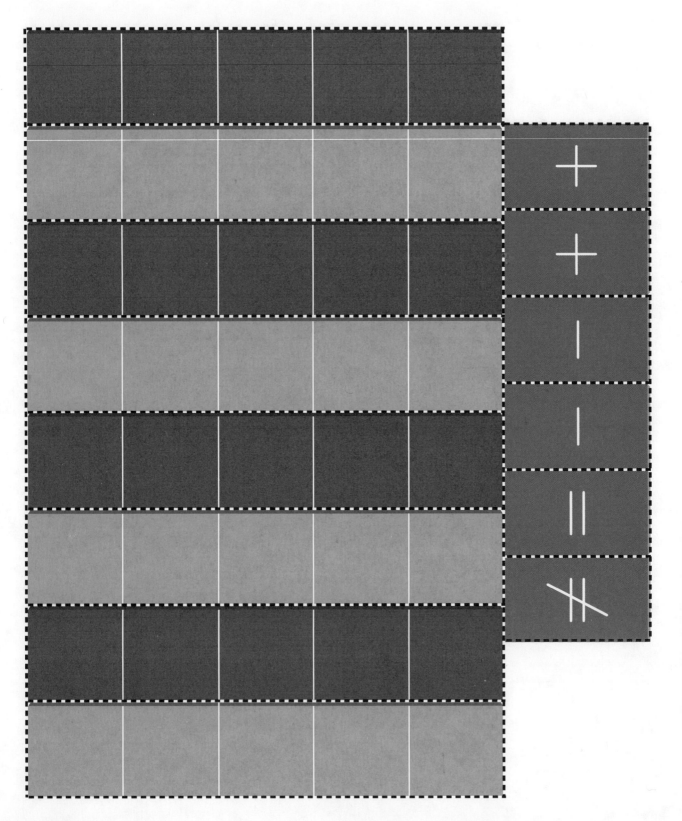

5-Square Tiles

Name _____

Use a 5-group. Write the number.

1

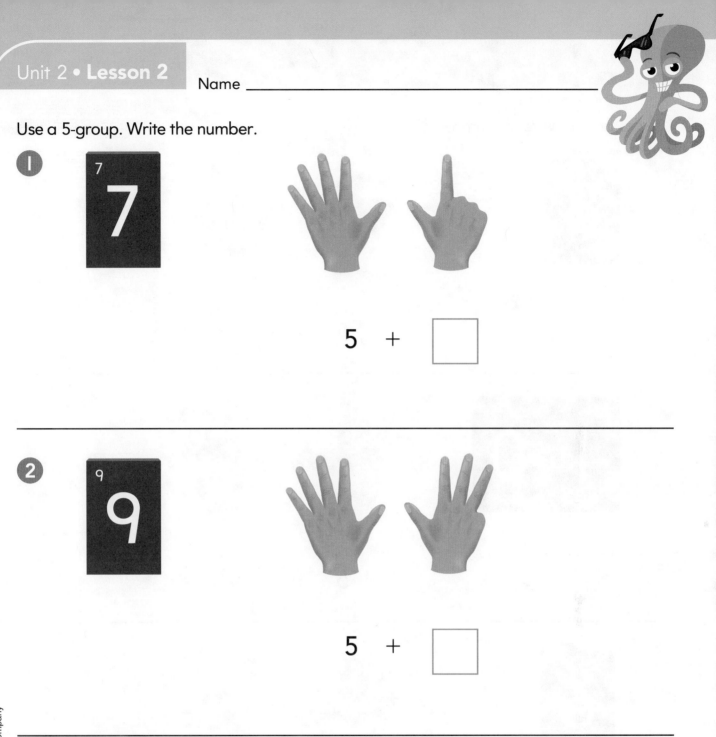

7

5   +   ☐

2

9

5   +   ☐

3

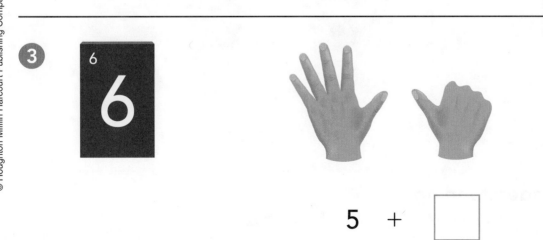

6

5   +   ☐

Relate Objects and Numbers 6–10 **73**

Use a 5-group. Write the number.

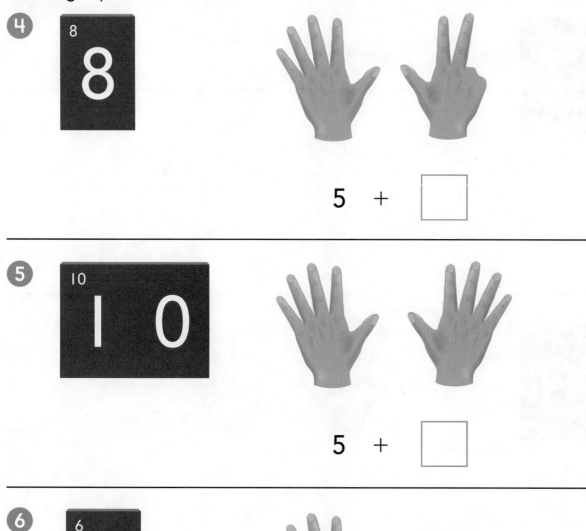

④ 8

8

5   +   ☐

⑤ 10

10

5   +   ☐

⑥ 6

6

5   +   ☐

© Houghton Mifflin Harcourt Publishing Company

✔ **Check Understanding**

TEACHER: What number do you need to add to a 5-group to get 8?

Relate Objects and Numbers 6–10

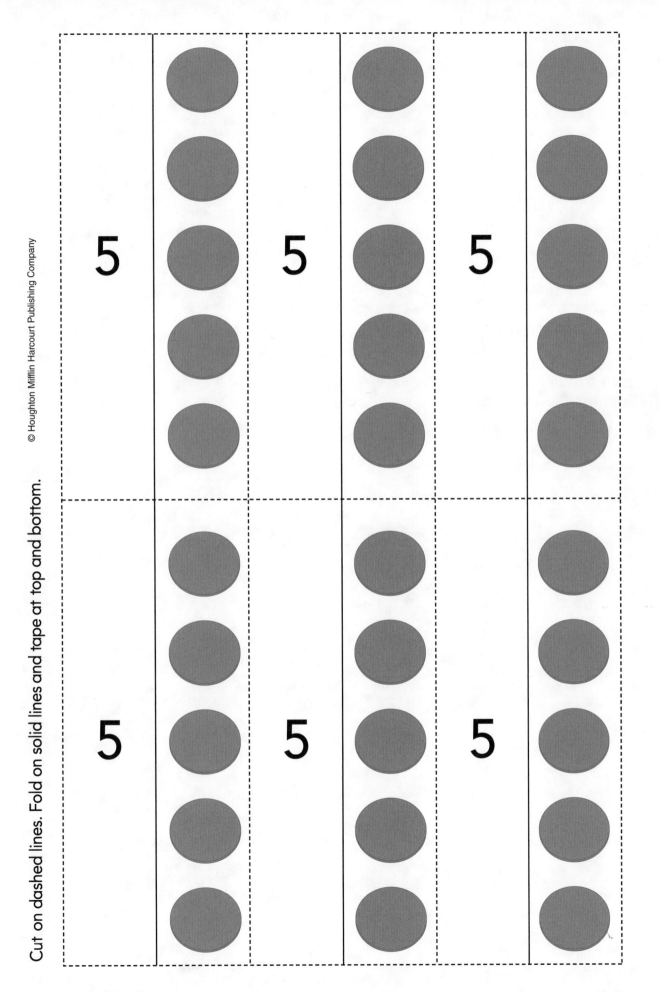

Cut on dashed lines. Fold on solid lines and tape at top and bottom.

5-Counter Strips **77**

5-Counter Strips

Name _____

Use 5-groups.

Write the number of extra counters.

1

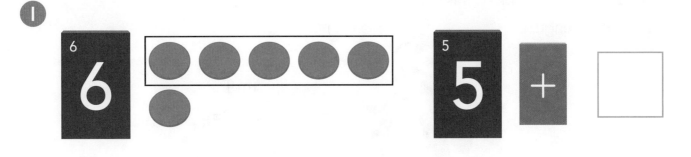

2

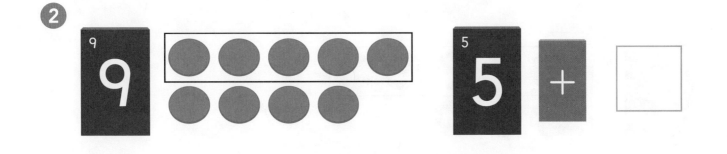

3

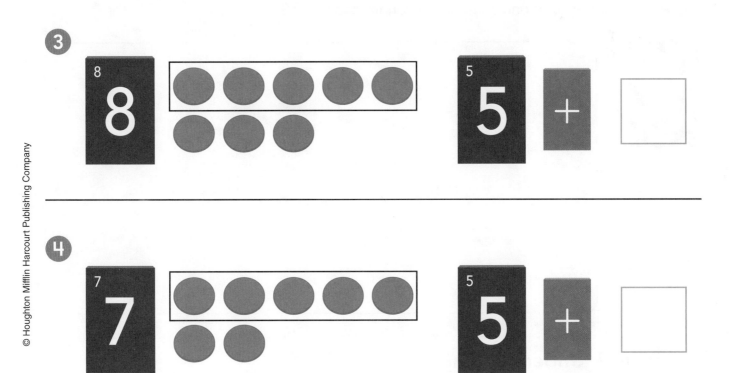

4

Puzzled Penguin used a 5-Counter Strip and some extra counters to show 7.

Did Puzzled Penguin make a mistake?

Help Puzzled Penguin.

Am I correct?

7

Draw a 5-Counter Strip and some extra counters to show 9.

9

✓ Check Understanding

TEACHER: Look at the grouping for the number 7. Why does showing a 5-group make it easier to see the number?

Name _____

Write the number 6.

6 6 6 6 6 6 6 6

6

6   6   6

6

Draw 6 objects.	Draw 6 balls.

        Add and Subtract with Family Math Stories **81**

Ring 6 hats.

Write the number 6.

$6 \quad 6 \quad 6 \quad 6 \quad 6 \quad 6 \quad 6 \quad 6$

6

✓ **Check Understanding**

TEACHER: Ring the number of marbles.

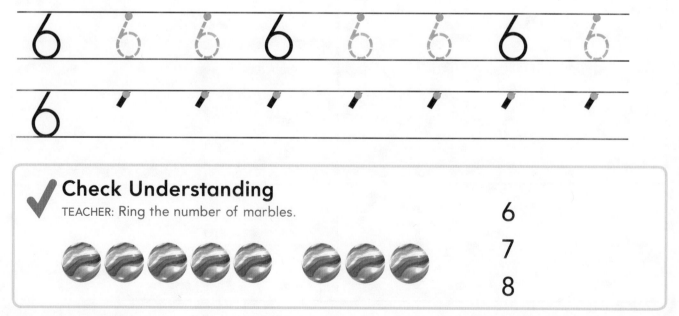

6

7

8

© Houghton Mifflin Harcourt Publishing Company

Add and Subtract with Family Math Stories

Name _____

Tell an addition or subtraction story.

Make a drawing to show how many balloons in all.

Addition and Subtraction Stories: Playground Scenario **83**

Connect the dots in order. Use **straight lines**.

VOCABULARY
straight lines

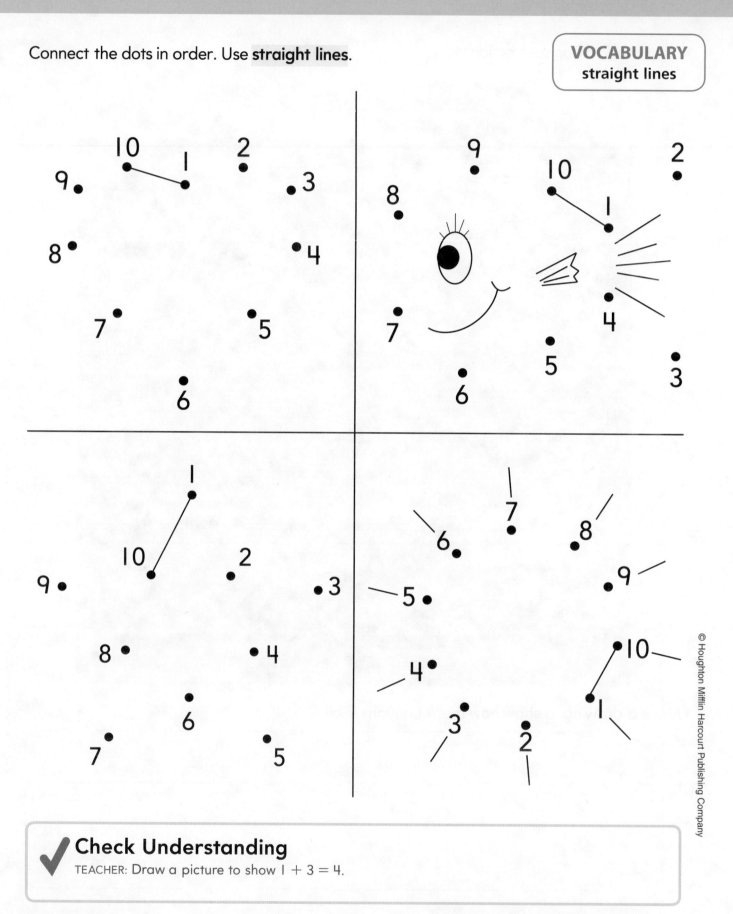

✔ **Check Understanding**

TEACHER: Draw a picture to show $1 + 3 = 4$.

Addition and Subtraction Stories: Playground Scenario

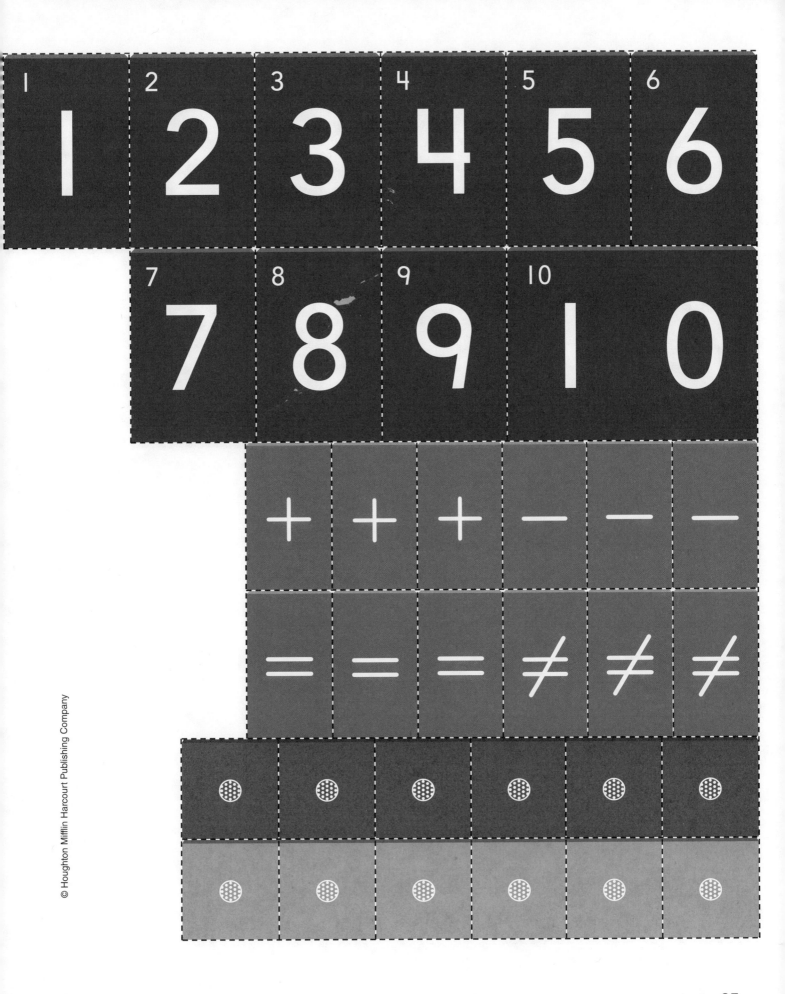

+/− Tiles, =/≠ Tiles **85**

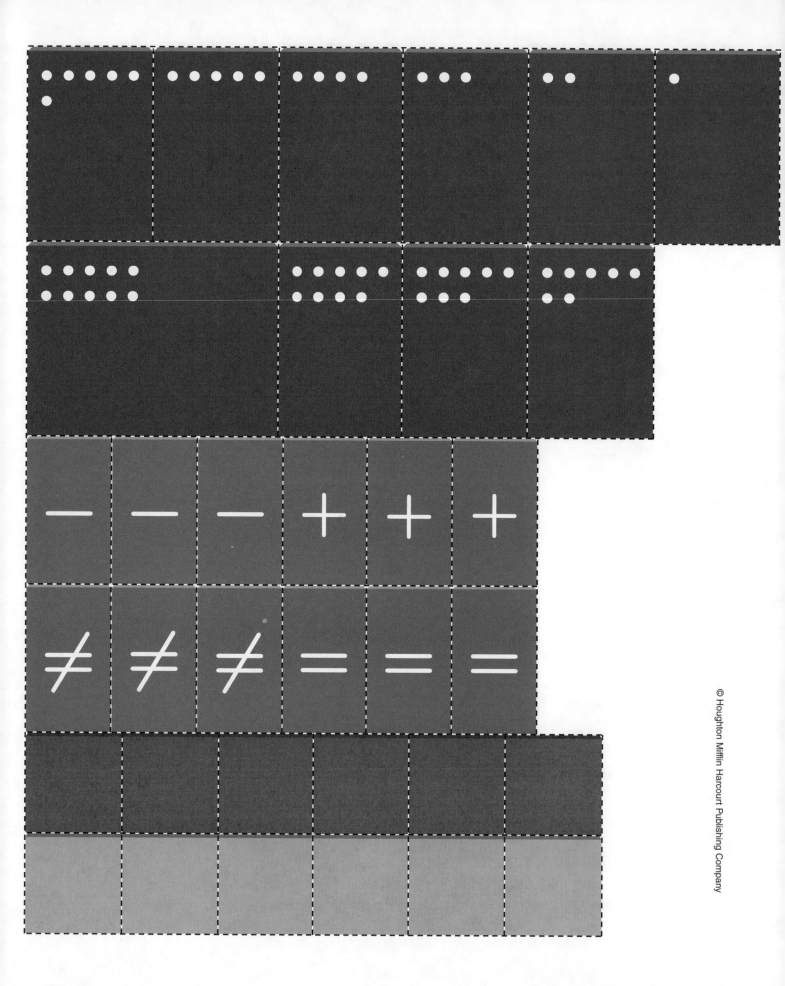

+/− Tiles, =/≠ Tiles

Name _____

Write the numbers 2 and 5.

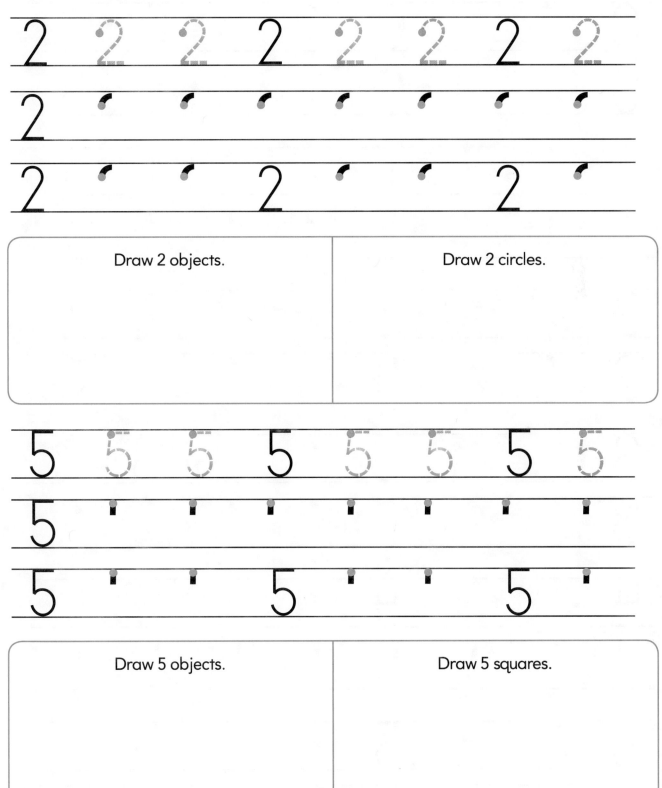

2 2 2 2 2 2 2 2

2

2   2   2

Draw 2 objects. | Draw 2 circles.

5 5 5 5 5 5 5 5

5

5   5   5

Draw 5 objects. | Draw 5 squares.

Numbers 6–10 **87**

Write numbers 0 through 5 in order. Use the Number Parade to help.

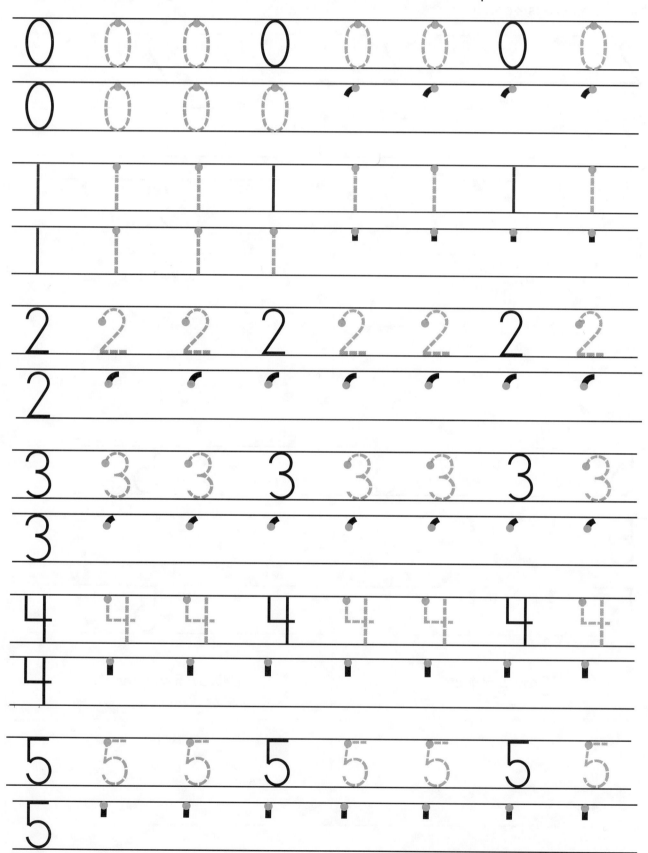

© Houghton Mifflin Harcourt Publishing Company

Name _____

Listen to the directions.

Look at the children in line.

See who is first, second, third, fourth, and fifth.

Color the rest of the page.

Numbers 6–10 **89**

Listen to the directions.

Find who is first, second, third, fourth, fifth,

sixth, seventh, eighth, ninth, and tenth in line.

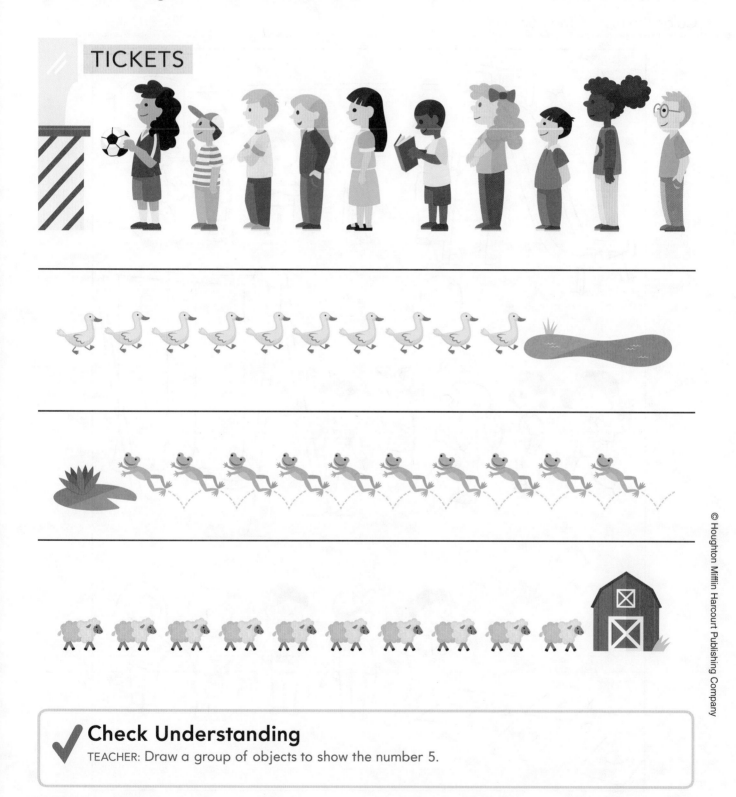

✔ Check Understanding

TEACHER: Draw a group of objects to show the number 5.

Name _____

Write the number 7.

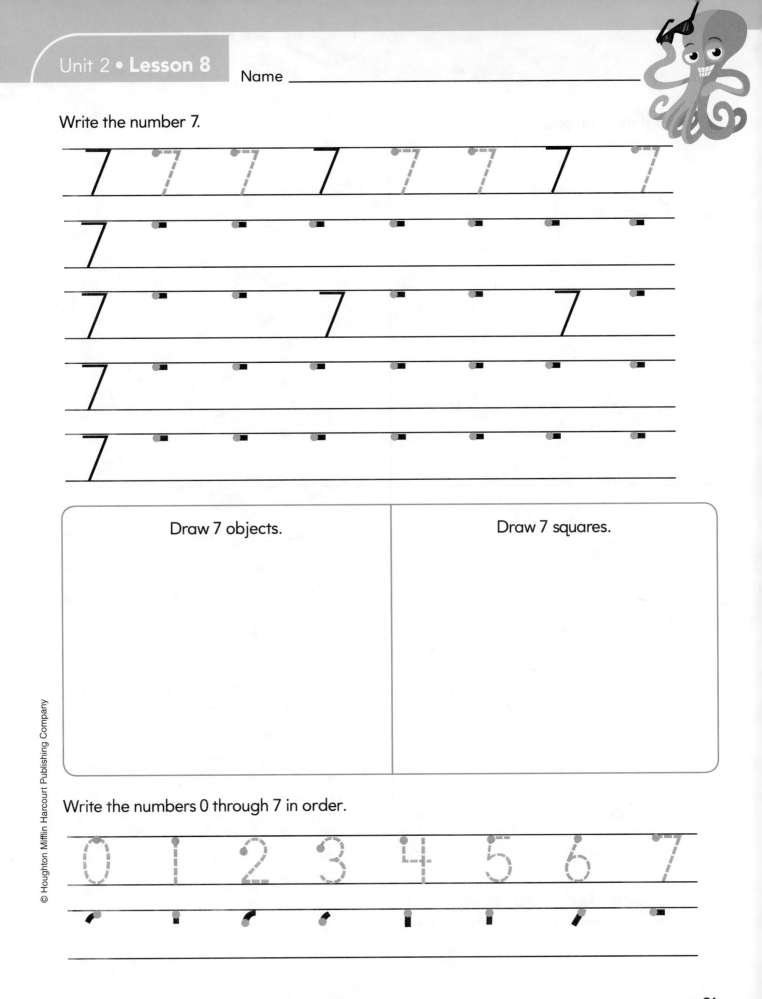

Draw 7 objects.

Draw 7 squares.

Write the numbers 0 through 7 in order.

0 1 2 3 4 5 6 7

Connect the dots in order.

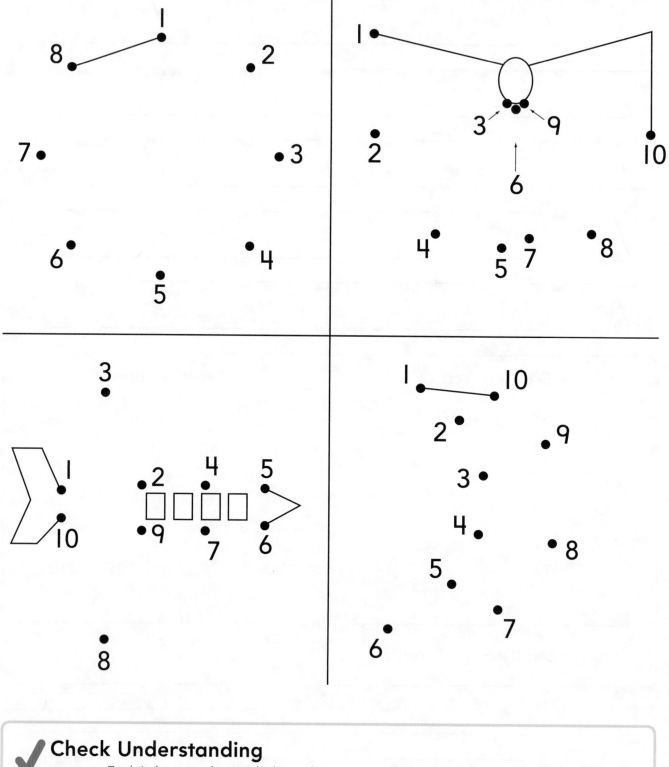

✔ Check Understanding

TEACHER: Explain how you know which number to go to next for the dot-to-dot drawings.

Name _____

Use a pencil or marker and trace each
number 2 times. Use the color blue to trace
the 6s and the color red to trace the 7s.

| 6 | ● ● ● ● ●   ● |
| 7 | ● ● ● ● ●   ● ● |

7 6 7 7 6 7 6

6 6 7 6 7

7 7 6 6 6 7 7

6 7 6 7 6

7 7 7 6 7 6 7

Write the numbers 1 through 7 in order.

Practice with 5-Groups **93**

Help Puzzled Penguin.

Did Puzzled Penguin make a mistake?

Look at the numbers below.

Did I make a mistake?

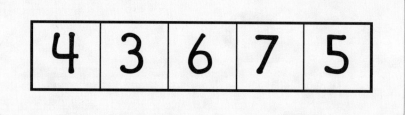

4	3	6	7	5

Write the numbers 3 through 7 in order.

Write the numbers 0 through 7 in order.

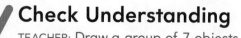

✔ **Check Understanding**

TEACHER: Draw a group of 7 objects.

Practice with 5-Groups

Name _____

Write the number 8.

8   8   8   8   8   8   8   8

8

8   8   8

8

8

Draw 8 objects. | Draw 8 rectangles.

Ring 8 objects.

Write the number 8.

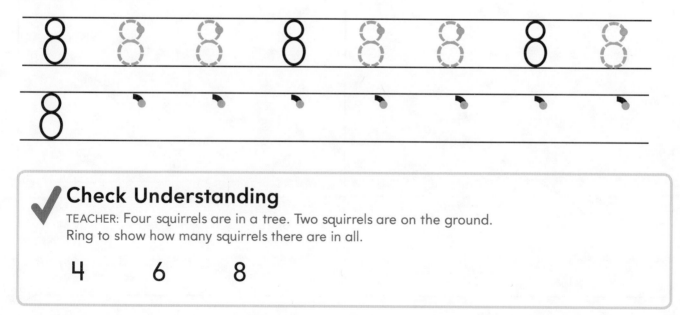

✔ Check Understanding

TEACHER: Four squirrels are in a tree. Two squirrels are on the ground. Ring to show how many squirrels there are in all.

4   6   8

Tell a math story.

Write the number 9.

9   9   9   9   9   9   9   9

9   9   9   9   9   9   9   9

9   9   9   9   9   9   9   9

9   9   9   9   9   9   9   9

9   9   9   9   9   9   9   9

Draw 9 objects.	Draw 9 circles.

© Houghton Mifflin Harcourt Publishing Company

✔ Check Understanding

TEACHER: Draw to show how many in all.

5 + 2

Addition and Subtraction Stories: Garden Scenario

Look at the counters.

Write the missing numbers.

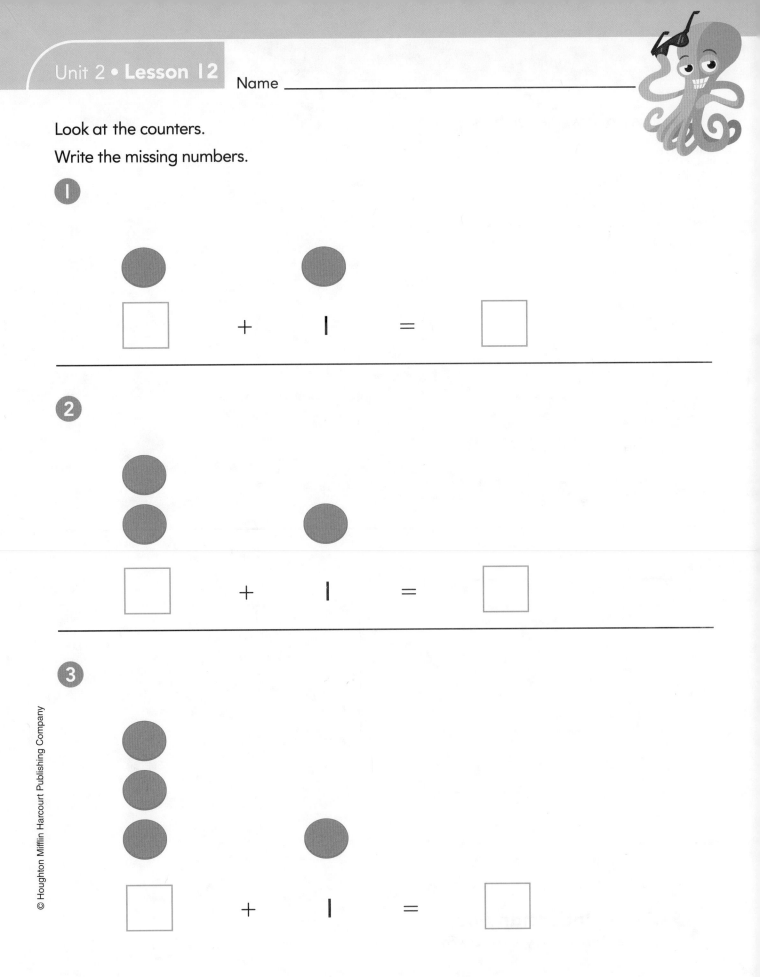

1

☐ + 1 = ☐

2

☐ + 1 = ☐

3

☐ + 1 = ☐

Draw circles to show the numbers.

How many in all?

Write the number.

4

$$4 \quad + \quad 1 \quad = \quad \boxed{}$$

5

$$5 \quad + \quad 1 \quad = \quad \boxed{}$$

✓ **Check Understanding**

TEACHER: Explain how you can use counters to show $7 + 1$. Then solve.

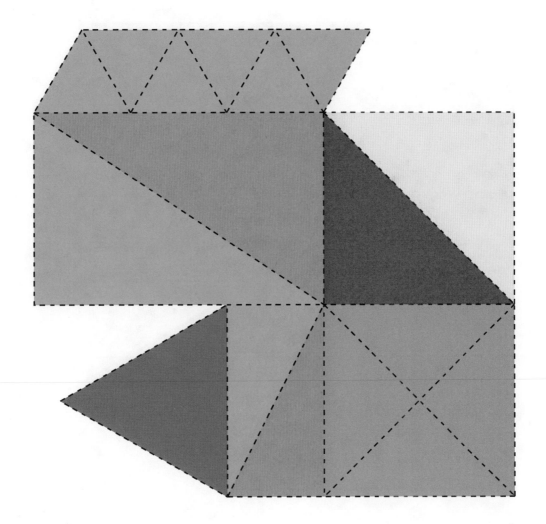

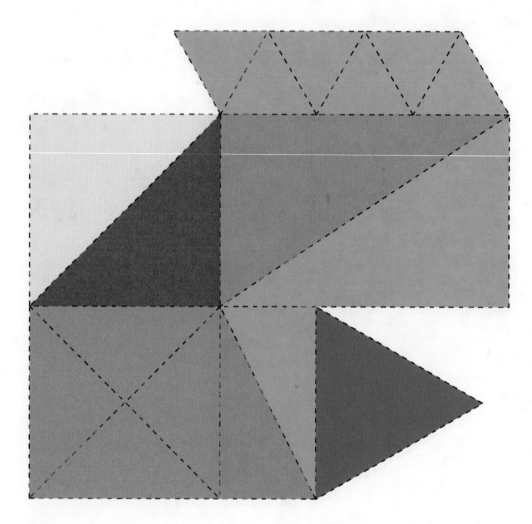

Discuss shapes you see.

Trace the shapes.

Draw the same shapes below the pictures.

Color the **triangles** you draw.

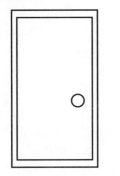

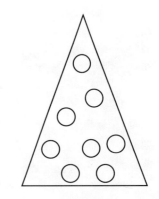

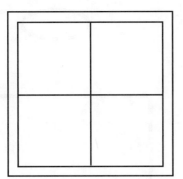

Name shapes you see.

Count the sides of each shape.

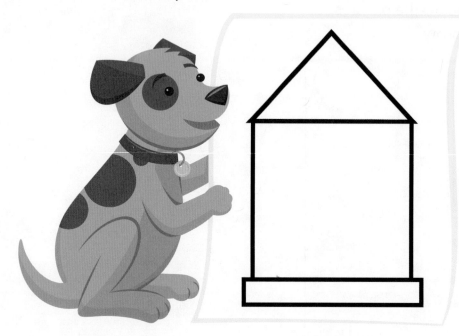

Color each shape needed to build the doghouse above.

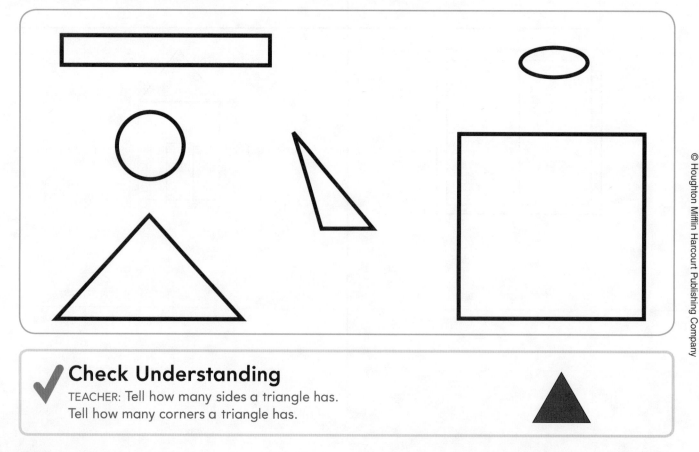

✔ Check Understanding

TEACHER: Tell how many sides a triangle has.
Tell how many corners a triangle has.

Identify Triangles

Name _____

Look at the counters.

Write the missing numbers.

1

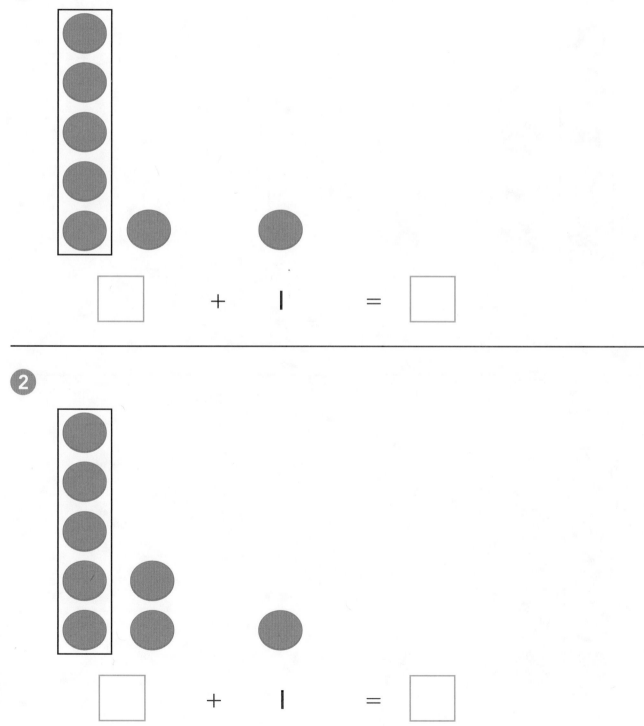

☐ + 1 = ☐

2

☐ + 1 = ☐

Look at the counters.

Write the missing numbers.

3

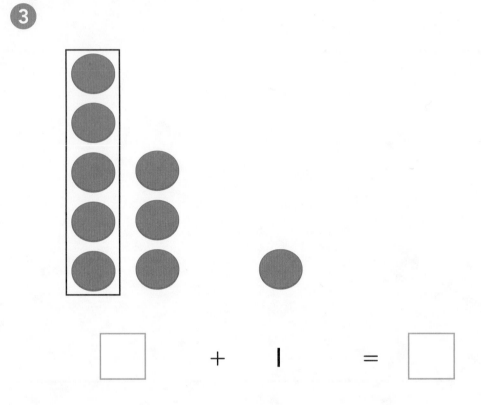

$$\boxed{} \quad + \quad 1 \quad = \quad \boxed{}$$

4

$$\boxed{} \quad + \quad 1 \quad = \quad \boxed{}$$

More Numbers 1 Through 10: The +1 Pattern

Name _____

5 Continue each pattern one more time.

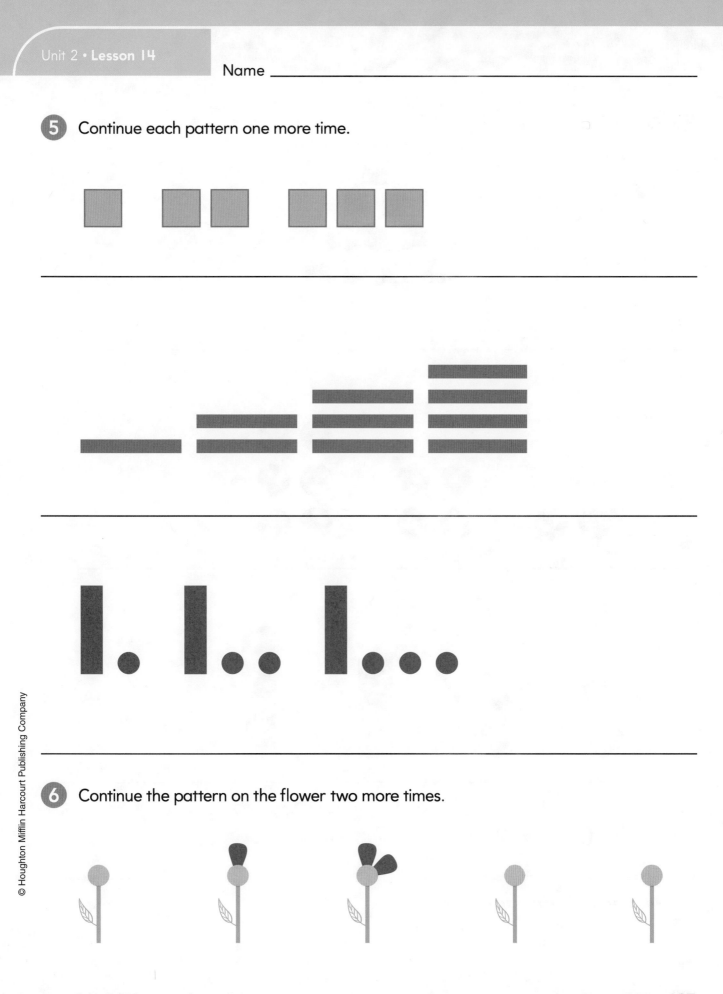

_____

_____

_____

6 Continue the pattern on the flower two more times.

7 Continue each pattern one more time.

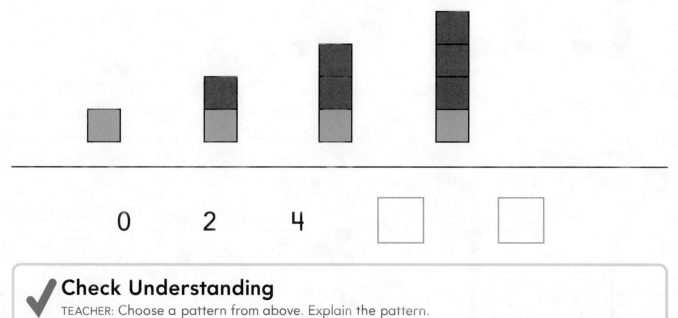

0   2   4   ▢   ▢

✓ Check Understanding
TEACHER: Choose a pattern from above. Explain the pattern.

More Numbers 1 Through 10: The +1 Pattern

Name _____

Write the number 10.

10 10 10 10 10

10

10

10

10

Draw 10 triangles.	Draw 10 circles.

Addition and Subtraction Stories: Family Experiences **109**

Ring 10 fish.

Practice writing the number 10.

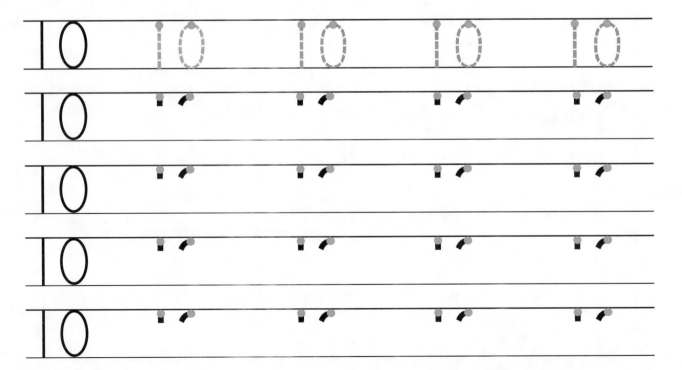

Addition and Subtraction Stories: Family Experiences

Cut on dashed lines. Fold on solid lines and tape at top and bottom.

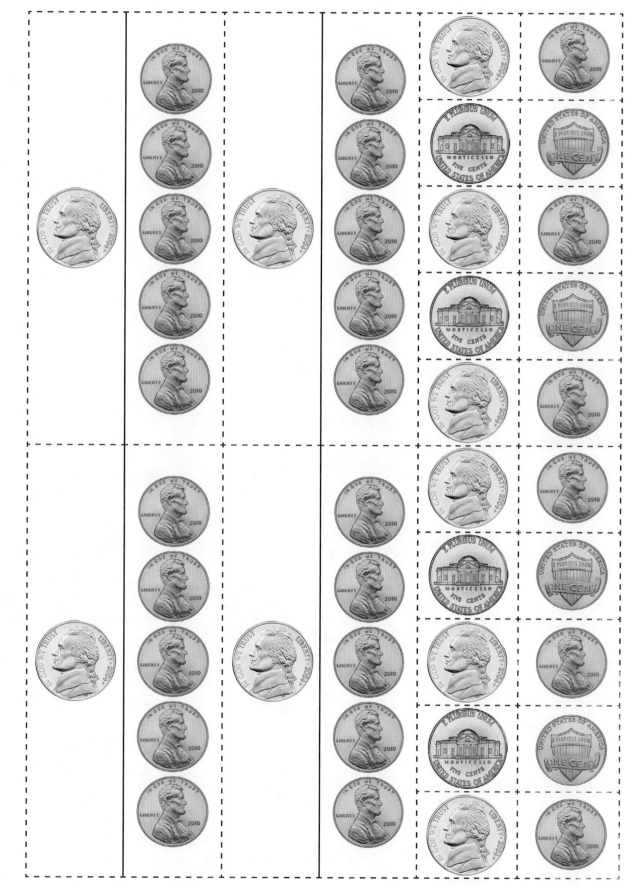

Nickel Strips, Nickels, Pennies

Nickel Strips, Nickels, Pennies

Name _____

VOCABULARY
nickel

A **nickel** is worth 5¢.

Trade each nickel for pennies.

Draw the number of pennies each group is worth.

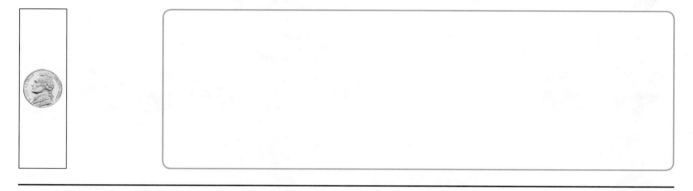

Write the number of cents.

Use your Nickel Strip to check.

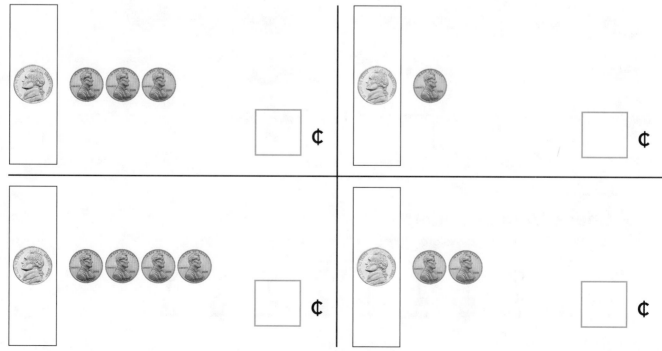

Addition and Subtraction Stories: Family Experiences **113**

Write the number of cents in each group.

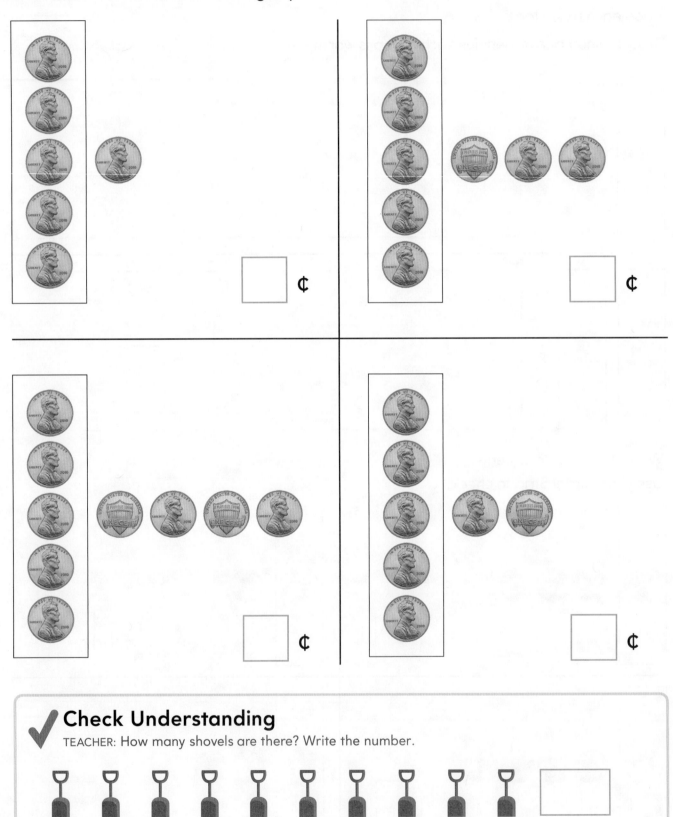

☑ **Check Understanding**

TEACHER: How many shovels are there? Write the number.

Addition and Subtraction Stories: Family Experiences

Use counters. Take away 1.

Write the number.

1 10 − 1 = ☐

2 9 − 1 = ☐

3 8 − 1 = ☐

4 7 − 1 = ☐

5 6 − 1 = ☐

6 5 − 1 = ☐

Use counters. Take away 1.

Write the number.

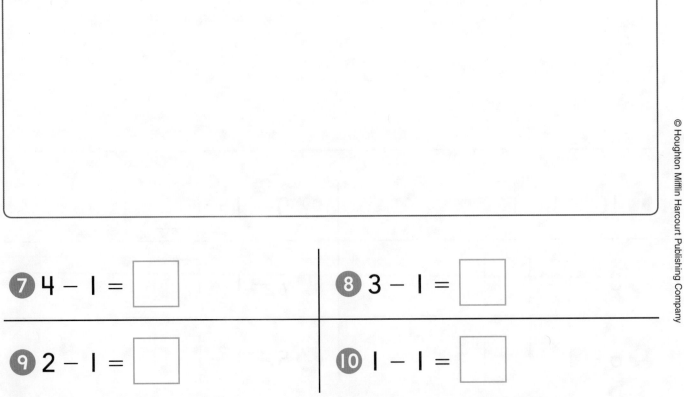

7 4 − 1 = ☐

8 3 − 1 = ☐

9 2 − 1 = ☐

10 1 − 1 = ☐

Numbers 1 Through 10: The −1 Pattern

Name _____

Continue each pattern one more time.

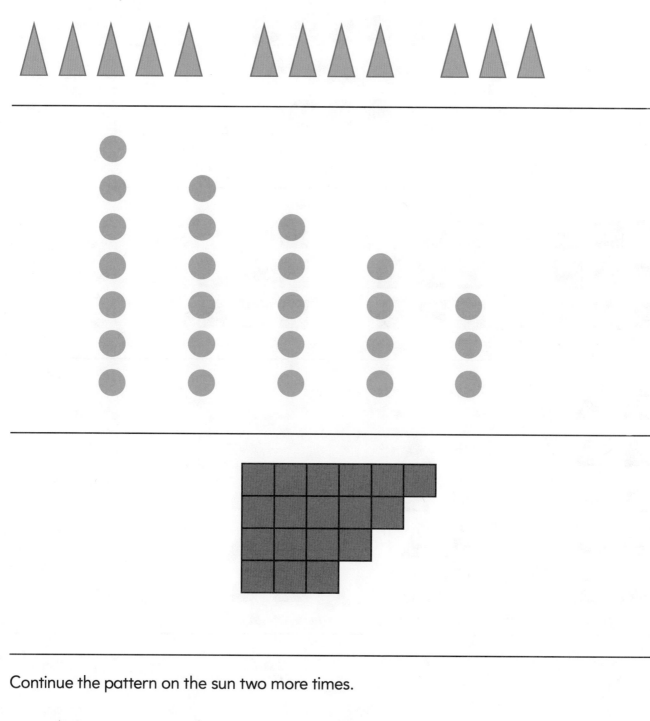

Continue the pattern on the sun two more times.

Numbers 1 Through 10: The −1 Pattern **117**

Continue each pattern one more time.

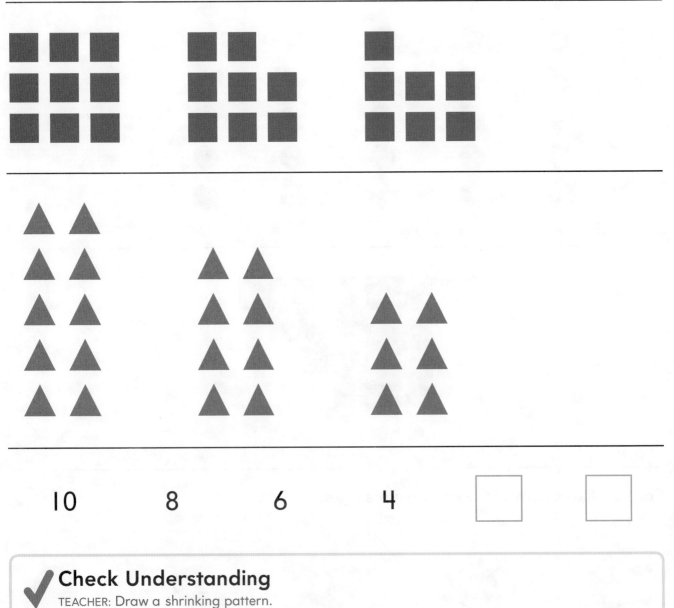

10   8   6   4   ☐   ☐

✓ **Check Understanding**
TEACHER: Draw a shrinking pattern.

Numbers 1 Through 10: The −1 Pattern

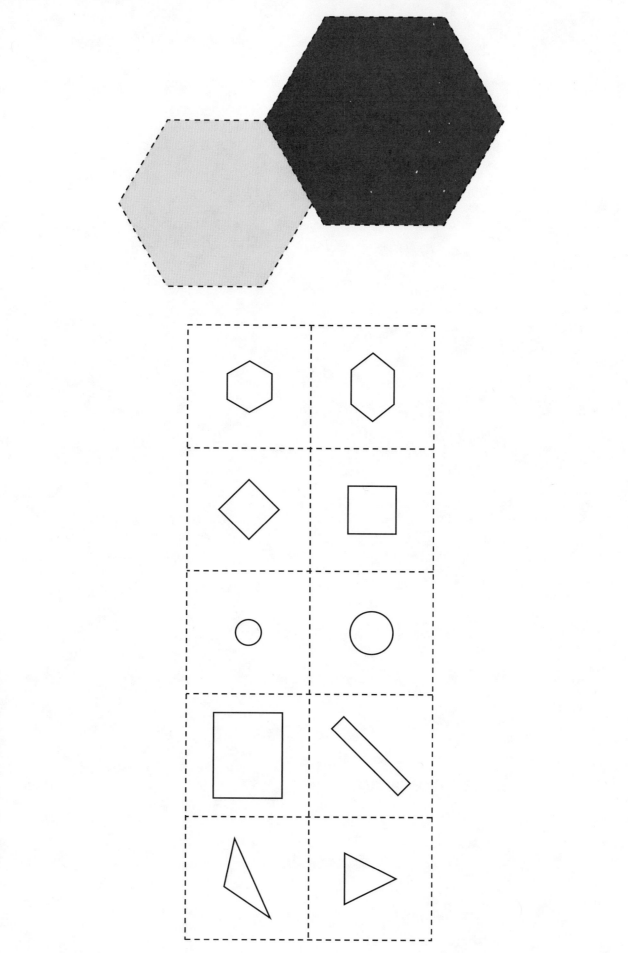

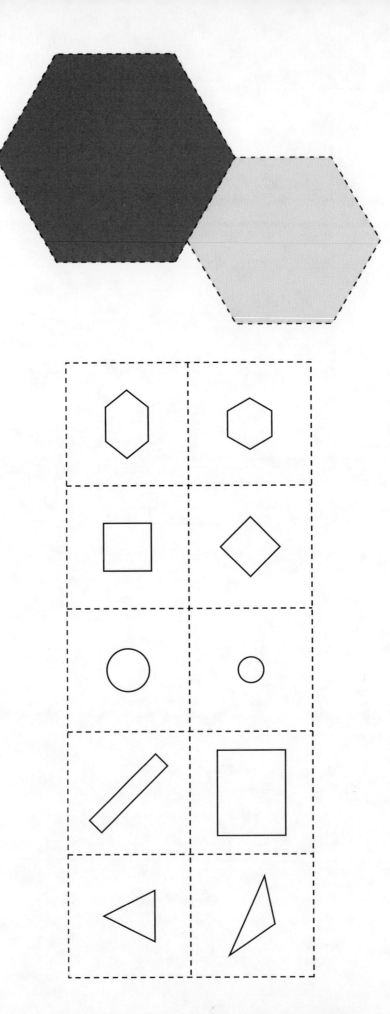

Hexagons

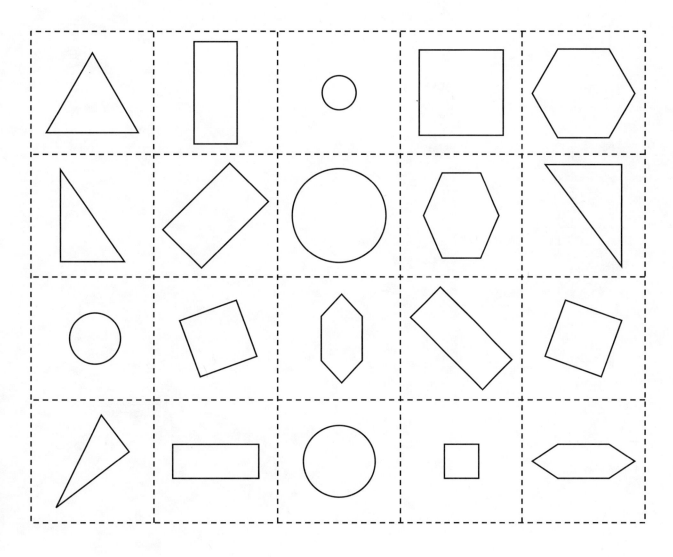

Identify Hexagons

Identify Hexagons

Color the shapes of one kind the same color as shown below.

VOCABULARY
hexagon

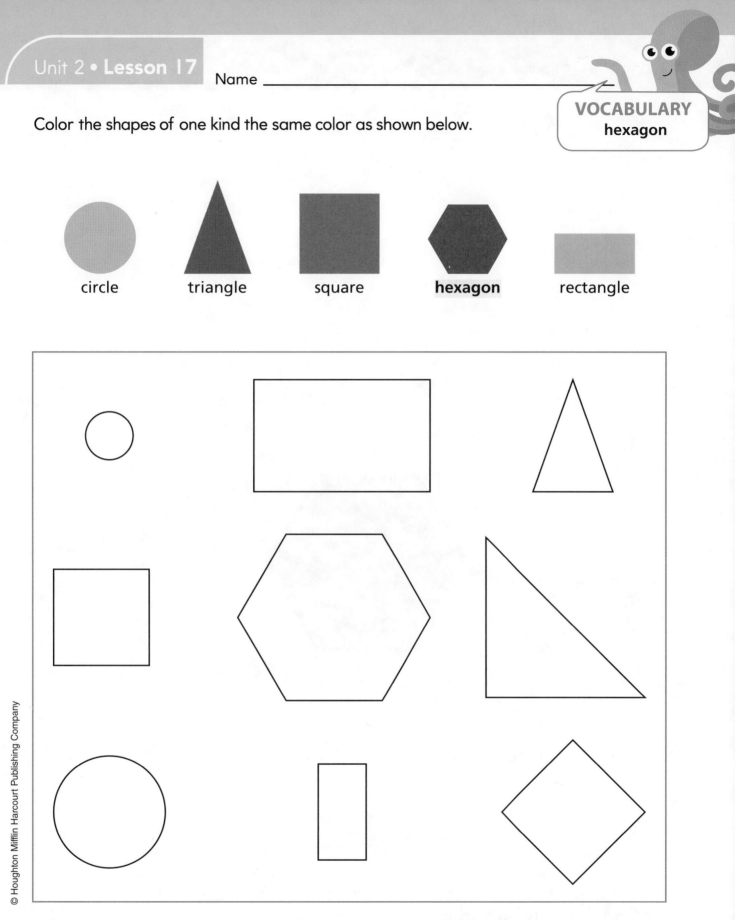

circle   triangle   square   **hexagon**   rectangle

Tell which shapes can have more than one color? Why?

✔ **Check Understanding**

TEACHER: What are some different words we can use to describe
the position of shapes?

Identify Hexagons

Name _____

Use a pencil or marker.
Trace each number two times.
Use the color red to trace the 8s.
Use the color blue to trace the 9s.

8

9

8   9   8   8   9   8   9   8   9

9   8   9   9   8   9   8   9

8   8   9   8   9   8   9   8

9   8   8   9   8   9   8   9

Write the numbers 1 through 10 in order.

Help Puzzled Penguin.

Puzzled Penguin was asked to write the number 6.

Did Puzzled Penguin write the number correctly?

Am I correct?

What number did Puzzled Penguin write?

How can we help Puzzled Penguin write the correct number?

Write the number for Puzzled Penguin.

Practice writing the number 6.

Practice writing the number 9.

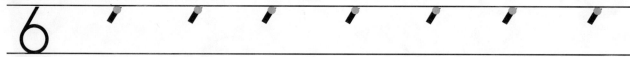

Write the numbers 6 through 10 in order.

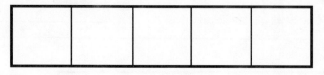

✓ **Check Understanding**

TEACHER: Write the number 6. Draw a group of objects to show the number.

© Houghton Mifflin Harcourt Publishing Company

Number Writing Practice

Name _____

Help Puzzled Penguin.

Did Puzzled Penguin make a mistake?

Look at the numbers below.

Did I make a mistake?

Cross out any numbers that are not in the correct order.

Help Puzzled Penguin write the numbers in the correct order.

Cross out any numbers that are not in the correct order.

0	1	2	3	4	5	6	7	9	8

Help Puzzled Penguin write the numbers in the correct order.

© Houghton Mifflin Harcourt Publishing Company

More Numbers 1 Through 10: The −1 Pattern

Write the numbers 1 through 10 in order.

| 1 | 2 | | 4 | | | 7 | | | 10 |

| | 2 | 3 | | 5 | 6 | | 8 | 9 | |

| | | | | | | | | | |

Write the numbers 0 through 9 in order.

| 0 | 1 | | 3 | 4 | | | 7 | | 9 |

| 0 | | 2 | | | 5 | 6 | | 8 | |

| | | | | | | | | | |

✓ ## Check Understanding

TEACHER: Tell which number comes before 6.
Tell which number comes after 7.

More Numbers 1 Through 10: The −1 Pattern

Name _____

Color the shapes of one kind the same color.
Count the number of each shape.
Write the number.

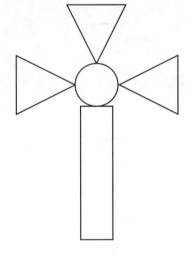

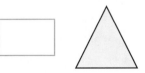

Draw a line to match each shape below to a shape in the picture.

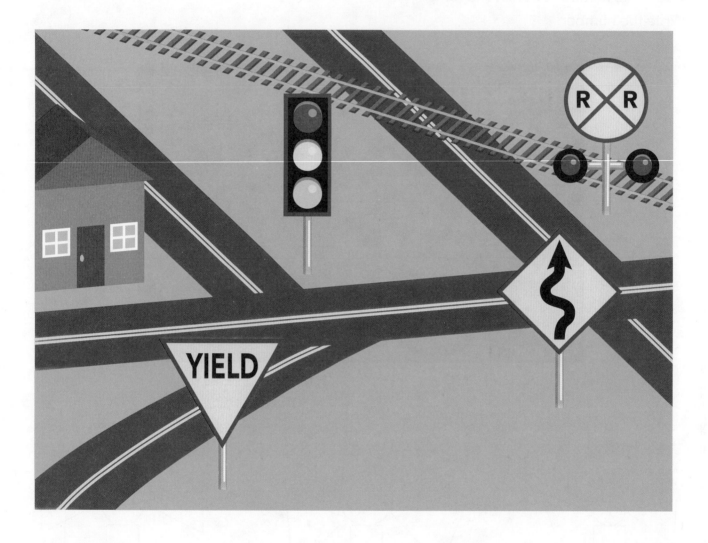

circle

rectangle

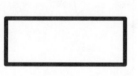

triangle

square

Focus on Problem Solving

1 Choose all the groups of the number.

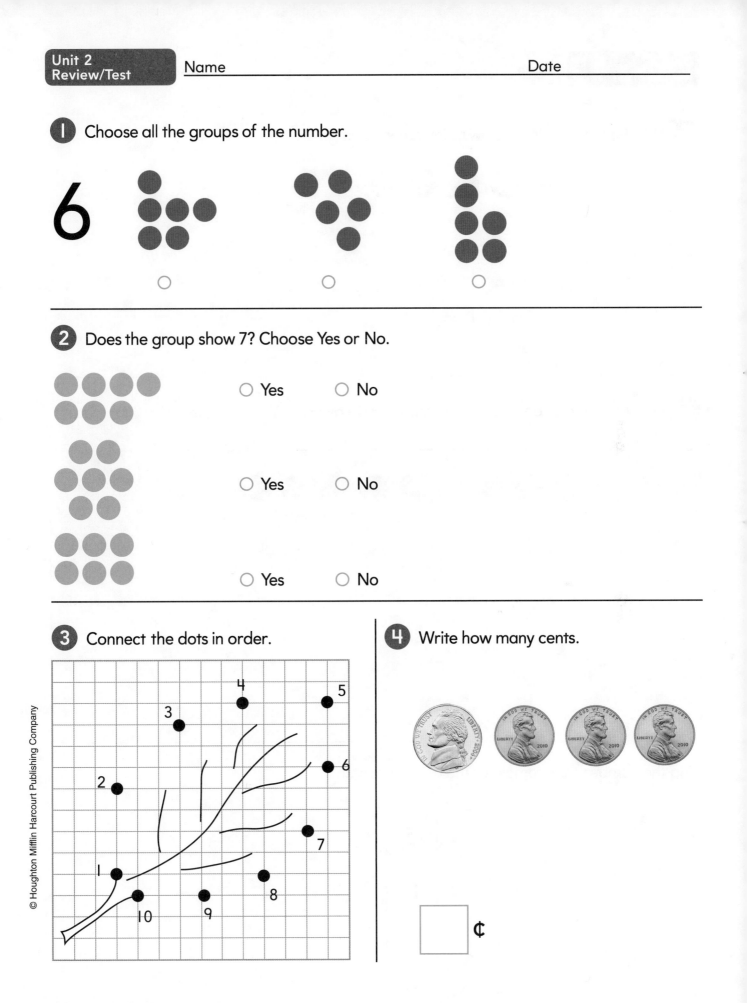

6   ○   ○   ○

2 Does the group show 7? Choose Yes or No.

○ Yes   ○ No

○ Yes   ○ No

○ Yes   ○ No

3 Connect the dots in order.

4 Write how many cents.

☐ ¢

5 Use the 5-group. Write how many green dots.

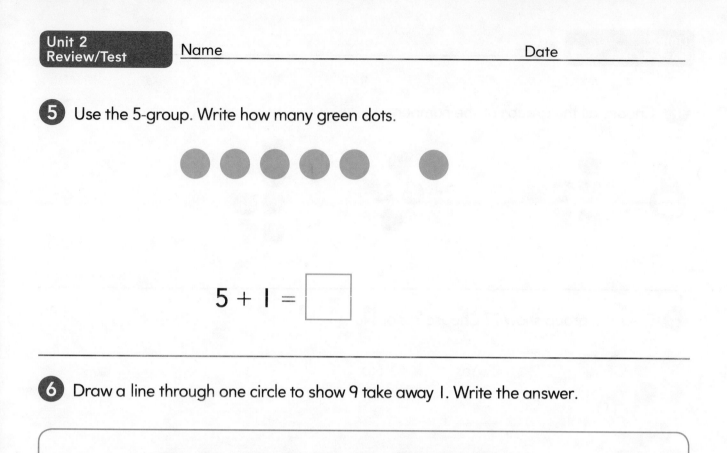

$$5 + 1 = \boxed{}$$

---

6 Draw a line through one circle to show 9 take away 1. Write the answer.

Ring the number that completes the number sentence.

$$9 - 1 = \begin{array}{|c|} \hline 7 \\ 8 \\ 9 \\ \hline \end{array}$$

7 Draw 4 triangles in the box. Write how many sides a triangle has.

A triangle has ☐ sides.

---

8 Draw a line under each hexagon.

9 Look at the number tiles. Write the numbers 6 through 10 in order.

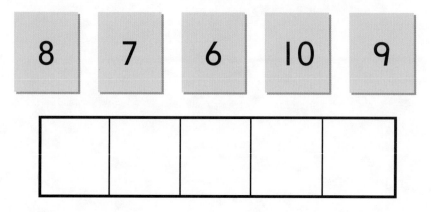

 Continue the pattern one more time.
Color the first square in each group blue.
How many squares did you color?

□   □ □   □ □ □

□ squares

© Houghton Mifflin Harcourt Publishing Company

Train Stories

Part A

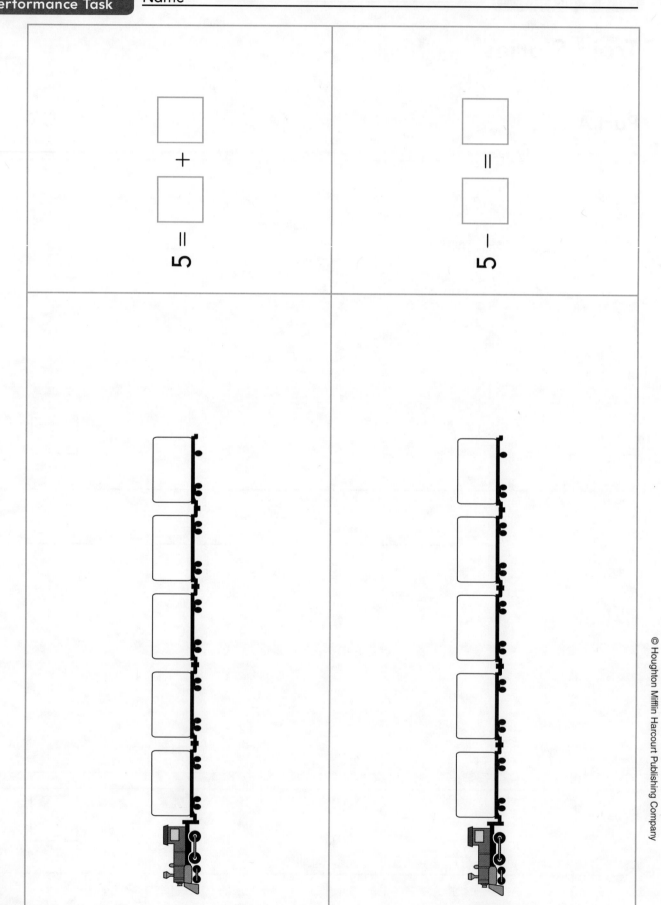

Part B

$5 = \boxed{} + \boxed{}$

$5 - \boxed{} = \boxed{}$

© Houghton Mifflin Harcourt Publishing Company

Dear Family:

Your child is starting a new unit on grouping concepts. These concepts provide a foundation for understanding basic math equations. In class, children will learn to find the ten in teen numbers ($17 = 10 + 7$), break apart numbers to find "partners" ($6 = 4 + 2$), recognize when numbers are equal or not equal, apply the concepts of *more* and *fewer*, and observe different attributes of shapes.

Being able to group numbers and shapes makes them easier to understand. You can help your child by practicing grouping concepts at home. Here is an example of an activity you can do with your child:

When cleaning up from play, have your child sort the objects before putting them away. Talk about the differences in size, shape, and color, and help your child place the items in groups based on these attributes. For example, the blocks below are sorted by size. They could also be sorted by color.

Thank you for your continued support.

Sincerely,
Your child's teacher

Estimada familia:

Su niño está empezando una nueva unidad que trata sobre los conceptos de agrupar. Estos conceptos son muy importantes para comprender las ecuaciones matemáticas básicas. Los niños aprenderán a hallar la decena en los números de 11 a 19 (17 = 10 + 7), a separar números para hallar "partes" (6 = 4 + 2), a reconocer si los números son iguales o no, a aplicar los conceptos de *más* y *menos* y a observar las características de las figuras.

Agrupar números y figuras facilita su comprensión. Usted puede ayudar a su niño practicando en casa los conceptos de agrupar. Aquí tiene un ejemplo de una actividad que pueden hacer:

Cuando estén guardando las cosas después de jugar, pida a su niño que separe los objetos en categorías. Háblele de las diferencias de tamaño, forma y color, y ayúdelo a colocar los objetos en grupos según estas características. Por ejemplo, los bloques que aparecen a continuación están agrupados según su tamaño. También se pueden agrupar según su color.

Gracias por su apoyo.

Atentamente,
El maestro de su niño

Numbers 1–10 and Math Stories: Park Scene

add	below
alike	beside
behind	between

The tree is **below** the bird.

$$3 + 2 = 5$$

The slide is **beside** the tree.

alike

The circle is **between** the square and the triangle.

The boy is **behind** the fence.

classify	equal to sign (=)
different	next to
dime	not equal to sign (≠)

$4 + 4 = 8$
4 plus 4 is **equal to** 8.

apples

not apples

The tree is **next to** the slide.

different

$6 \neq 8$
6 is **not equal to** 8.

front   back
10 cents or 10¢

sort	total
subtract	unknown
teen numbers	

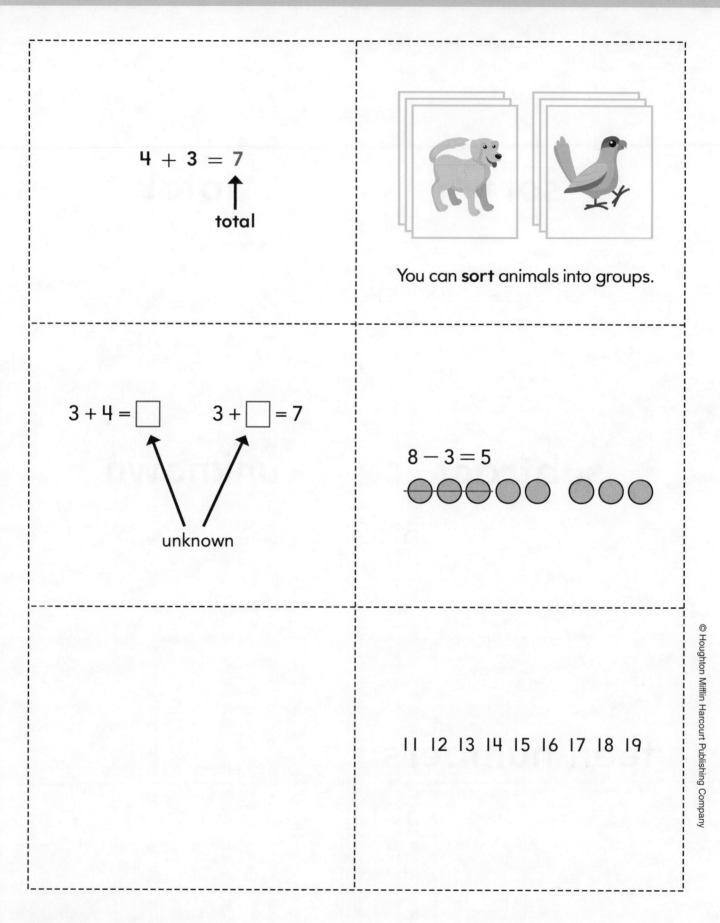

$4 + 3 = 7$

↑
total

You can **sort** animals into groups.

$3 + 4 = \square$ $3 + \square = 7$

unknown

$8 - 3 = 5$

11 12 13 14 15 16 17 18 19

Name _____

Color each group of 1 through 10 a different color.

Numbers 1–10 and Math Stories: Park Scene **139**

1 Connect the dots in order.

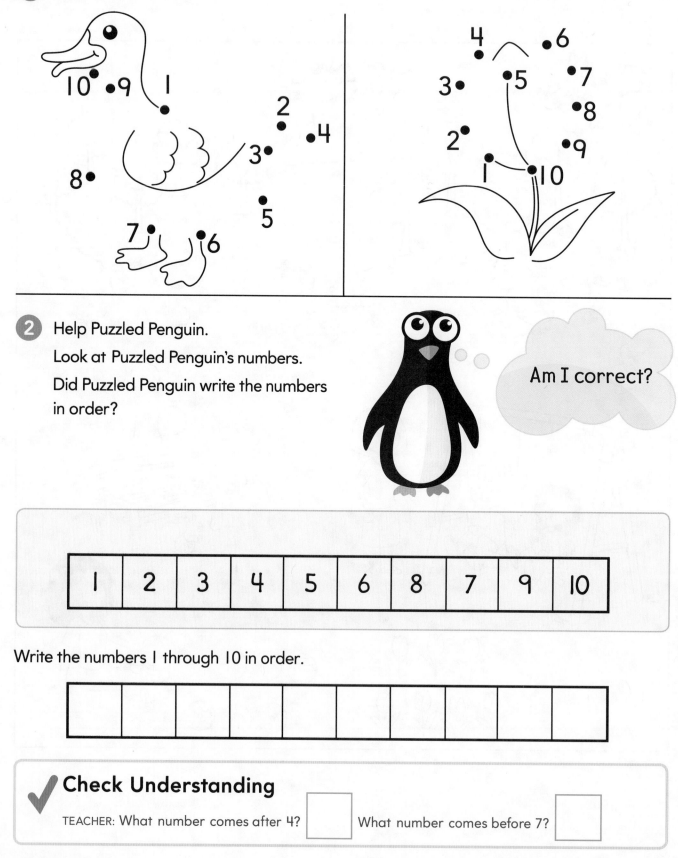

2 Help Puzzled Penguin.

Look at Puzzled Penguin's numbers.

Did Puzzled Penguin write the numbers in order?

Am I correct?

1	2	3	4	5	6	8	7	9	10

Write the numbers 1 through 10 in order.

✔ **Check Understanding**

TEACHER: What number comes after 4? ☐ What number comes before 7? ☐

Numbers 1–10 and Math Stories: Park Scene

Cut on dashed lines. **Fold** on solid lines and tape at top and bottom.

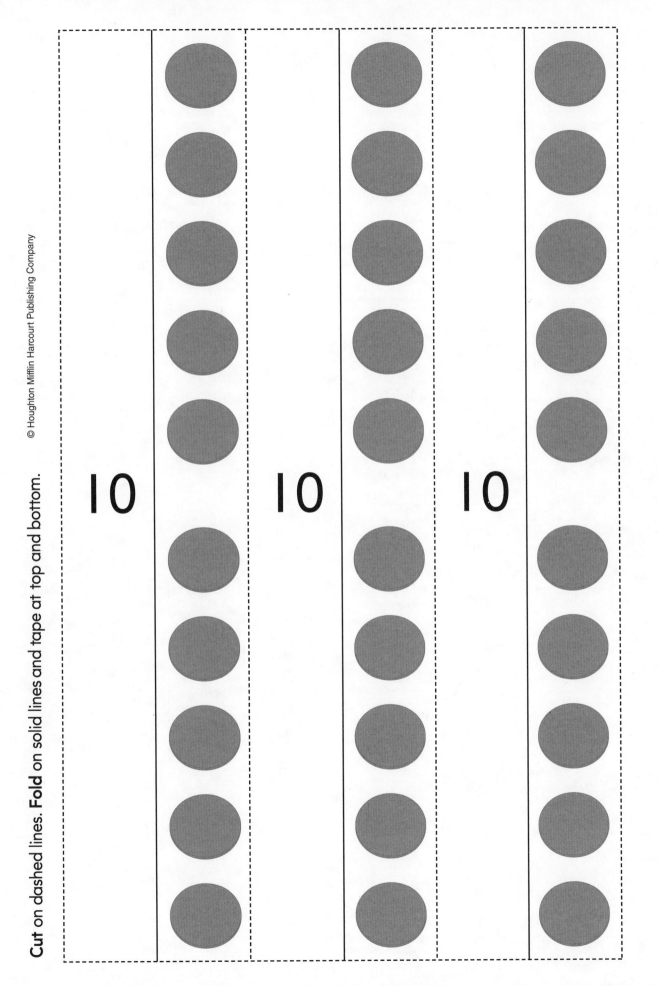

10

10

10

10-Counter Strips **141**

10-Counter Strips

Name _____

Connect the dots from 1 through 20 and color the Ten Bug.

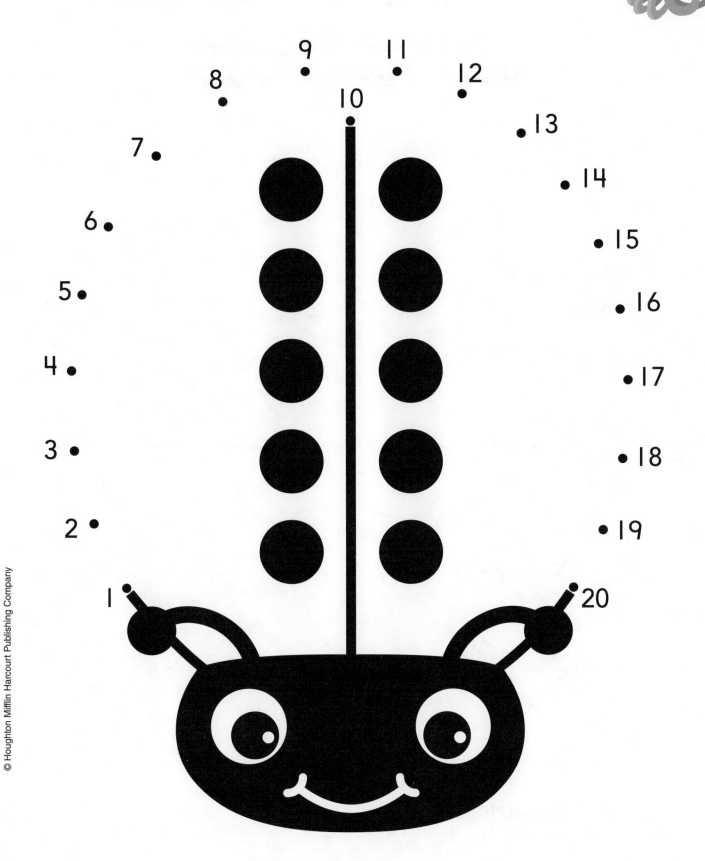

Groups of 10 **143**

Ring a group of 10 in each box. Count and color the items. Use the colors shown.

11—red   13—orange
12—blue   14—green

✔ **Check Understanding**

TEACHER: Explain how ringing a group of 10 helps you count.

Dear Family:

Your child is learning about partners of numbers. We call the number pairs that make up a number "partners" because they go together to make that number. For example,

6 has partners: 1 and 5   2 and 4   3 and 3

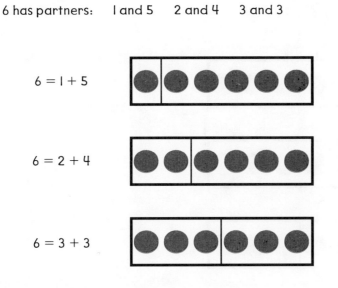

$$6 = 1 + 5$$

$$6 = 2 + 4$$

$$6 = 3 + 3$$

The partner idea is very important for understanding numbers. It will help your child understand addition and subtraction. You can help your child see partners in everyday life. When you have a small number of objects, for example, 5 crackers, you can ask your child to make the partners of 5. Your child can show 1 and 4 crackers and can also show 2 and 3 crackers. Doing this often with different objects will help your child understand numbers.

Thank you!

Sincerely,
Your child's teacher

Estimada familia:

Su niño está aprendiendo sobre las partes de los números. Llamamos "partes" a los pares de números que pueden juntarse para formar un determinado número. Por ejemplo,

6 tiene las partes: 1 y 5   2 y 4   3 y 3

6 = 1 + 5

6 = 2 + 4

6 = 3 + 3

La idea de las partes es muy importante para entender los números. Ayudará a su niño a entender la suma y la resta. Ud. puede ayudar a su niño a ver partes en la vida diaria. Cuando tenga un pequeño número de objetos, por ejemplo 5 galletas, puede pedirle a su niño que muestre las partes de 5. Su niño puede mostrar 1 galleta y 4 galletas y también 2 galletas y 3 galletas. Hacer esto a menudo con distintos objetos puede ayudar a su niño a entender los números.

¡Gracias!

Atentamente,
El maestro de su niño

Name _____

Write the 4 partners.

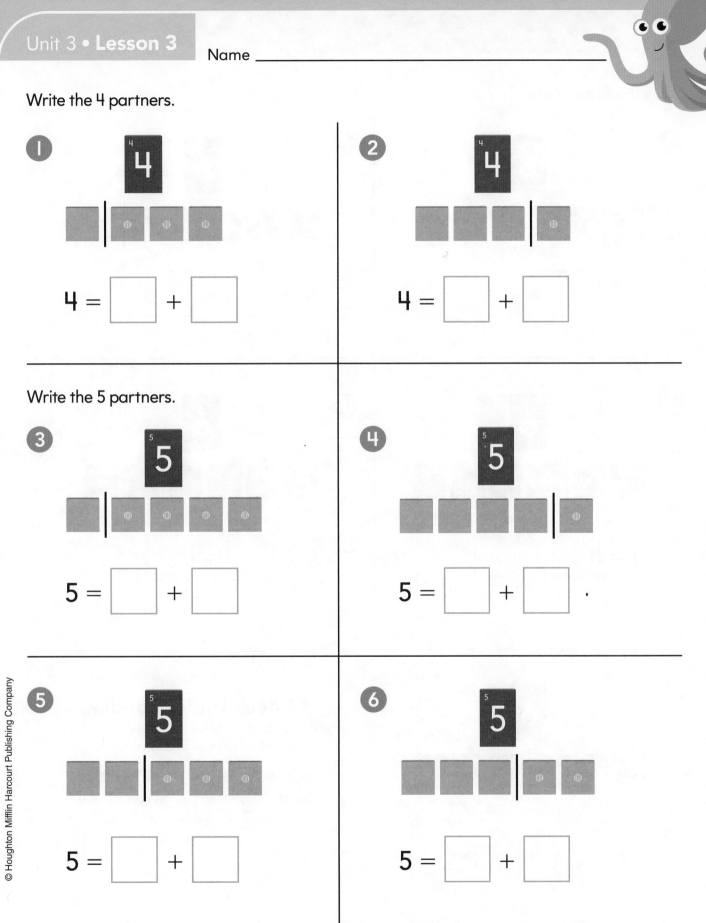

1

4 = ☐ + ☐

2

4 = ☐ + ☐

Write the 5 partners.

3

5 = ☐ + ☐

4

5 = ☐ + ☐ .

5

5 = ☐ + ☐

6

5 = ☐ + ☐

Explore Partners Through 6 **147**

Write the 6 partners.

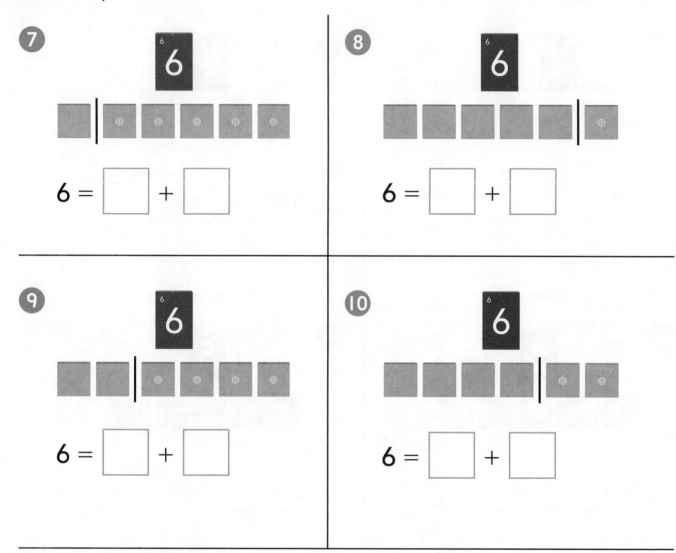

⑦

6 = ☐ + ☐

⑧

6 = ☐ + ☐

⑨

6 = ☐ + ☐

⑩

6 = ☐ + ☐

⑪

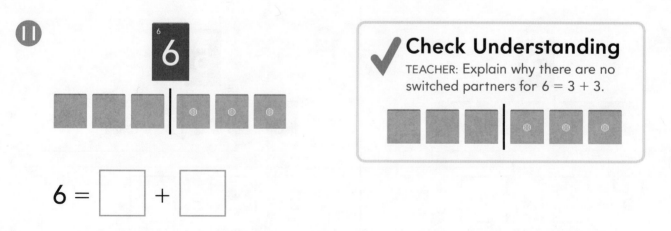

6 = ☐ + ☐

✔ **Check Understanding**

TEACHER: Explain why there are no switched partners for 6 = 3 + 3.

Explore Partners Through 6

Name _____

Count how many. Write the number.

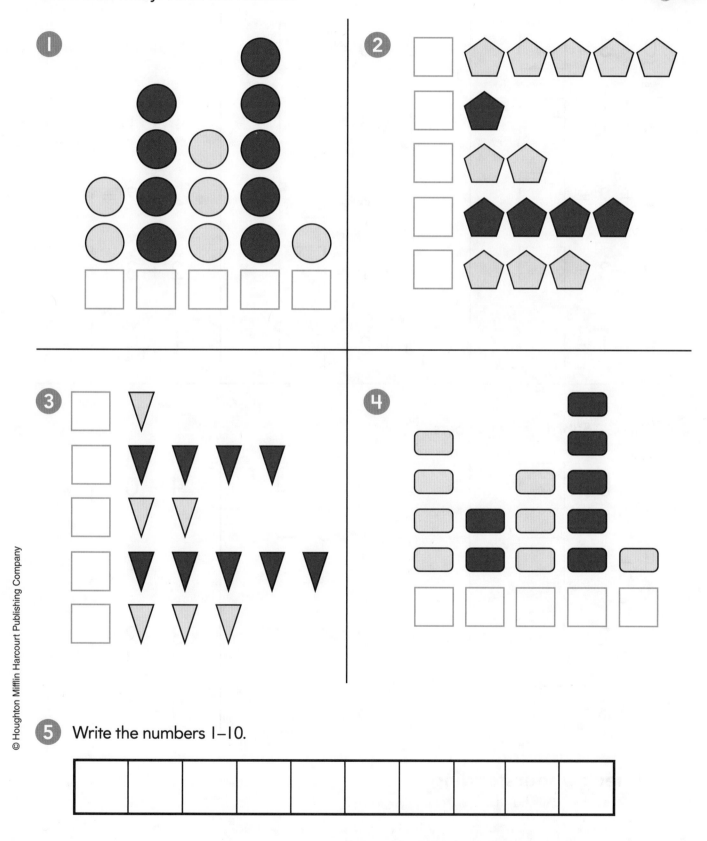

5 Write the numbers 1–10.

Addition and Subtraction Stories: Park Scene **149**

VOCABULARY
add
subtract

6 PATH to FLUENCY **Add** the numbers.

0 + 3 = ☐   2 + 0 = ☐   4 + 0 = ☐

2 + 1 = ☐   1 + 4 = ☐   1 + 1 = ☐

0 + 2 = ☐   1 + 2 = ☐   2 + 2 = ☐

0 + 3 = ☐   3 + 1 = ☐   2 + 3 = ☐

4 + 1 = ☐   5 + 0 = ☐   1 + 4 = ☐

7 PATH to FLUENCY **Subtract** the numbers.

3 − 0 = ☐   2 − 0 = ☐   4 − 0 = ☐

4 − 1 = ☐   5 − 1 = ☐   1 − 1 = ☐

5 − 2 = ☐   4 − 2 = ☐   3 − 2 = ☐

3 − 3 = ☐   5 − 3 = ☐   4 − 3 = ☐

✔ **Check Understanding**
TEACHER: Explain what the + sign and − sign mean.

Dear Family:

When children first start counting, they count objects one at a time. Helping children see 5-groups and 10-groups enables them to understand larger (greater) numbers. We are learning that if we can see groups of objects as 5-groups and 10-groups, then we can understand greater numbers. Children learn to make these groups with objects. Later, they will see them as organized groups in their minds.

Your child is learning that the teen numbers 11, 12, 13, 14, 15, 16, 17, 18, and 19 each have a 10 inside: $11 = 10 + 1$, $12 = 10 + 2$, and so on through $19 = 10 + 9$.

Have your child practice counting groups of objects. Your child can find and separate the 10-group from the total quantity to see the 10 hiding inside the teen number.

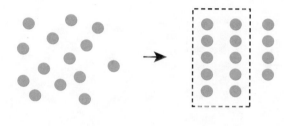

fourteen   is   ten and four

Your child can then show this number by using the number cards.

Thank you for your cooperation!

Sincerely,
Your child's teacher

Estimada familia:

Cuando los niños empiezan a contar, suelen contar los objetos uno por uno. Ayudarlos a ver los objetos en grupos de 5 y grupos de 10, les facilita el aprendizaje de números más grandes (mayores). Estamos aprendiendo que si podemos ver grupos de objetos como grupos de 5 y grupos de 10, entonces podemos entender números más grandes. Los niños aprenden a formar estos grupos con objetos. Más adelante, los verán mentalmente como grupos organizados.

Su niño está aprendiendo que los números 11, 12, 13, 14, 15, 16, 17, 18 y 19 contienen 10: 11 = 10 + 1, 12 = 10 + 2, y así sucesivamente, hasta 19 = 10 + 9.

Pida a su niño que practique contando grupos de objetos. Su niño puede separar el grupo de 10 de la cantidad total, para ver el 10 escondido en los números de 11 a 19.

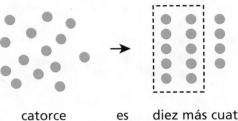

catorce   es   diez más cuatro

Después, su niño puede mostrar este número usando las tarjetas de números.

¡Gracias por su colaboración!

Atentamente,
El maestro de su niño

© Houghton Mifflin Harcourt Publishing Company

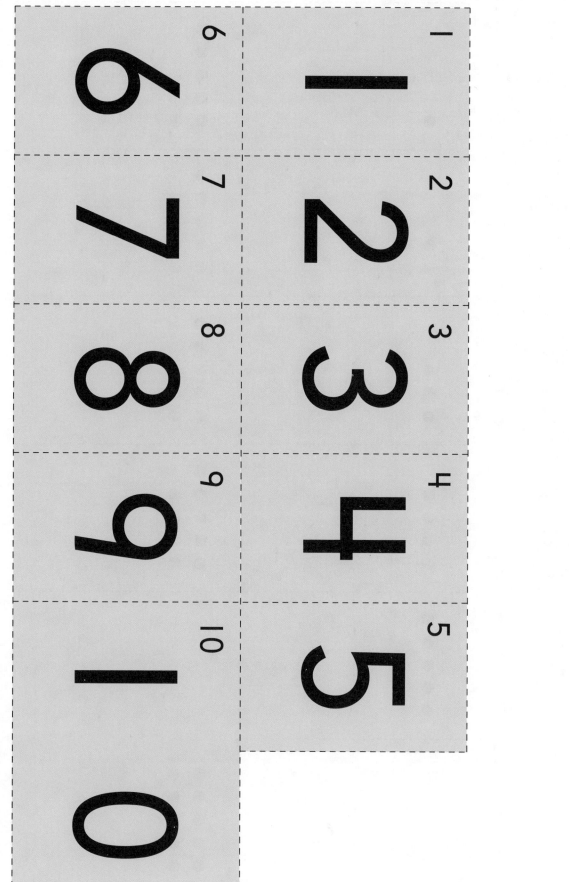

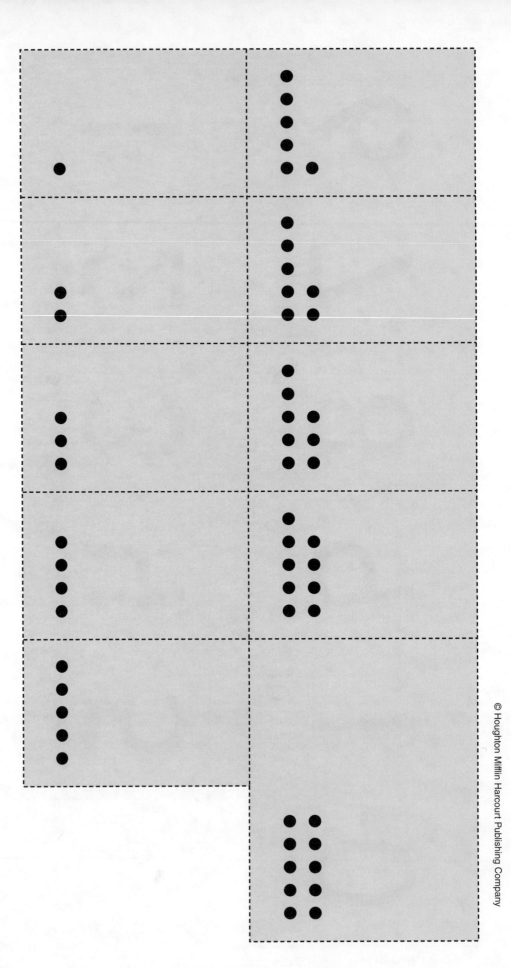

At Home Number Cards

Name _____

1 Draw the circles on the Number Parade. Use a 5-group.

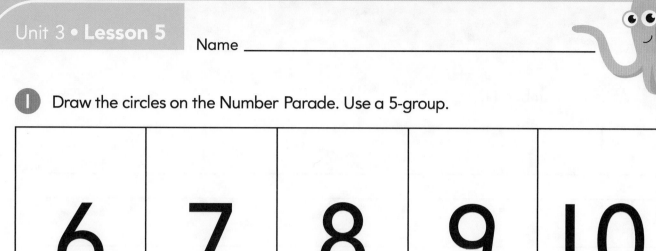

| 6 | 7 | 8 | 9 | 10 |

2 Use the 5-group. Draw to show the number.

3 Write the number.

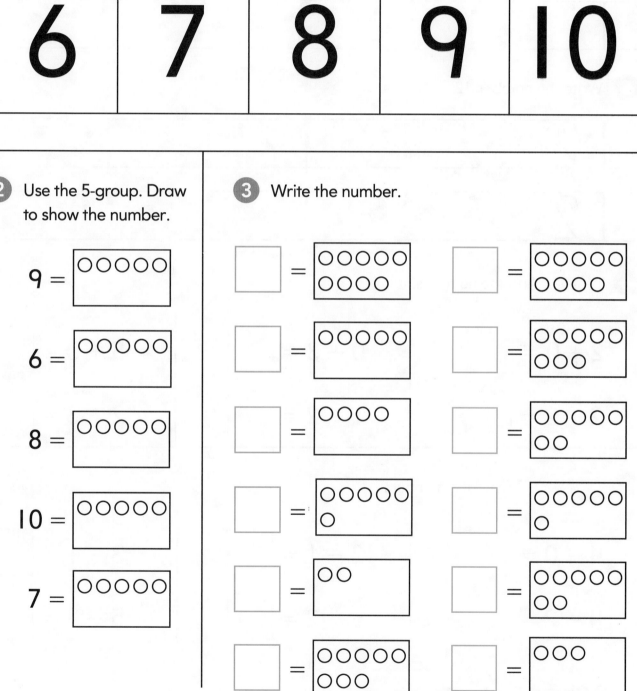

$9 =$

$6 =$

$8 =$

$10 =$

$7 =$

4 Write the number 11.

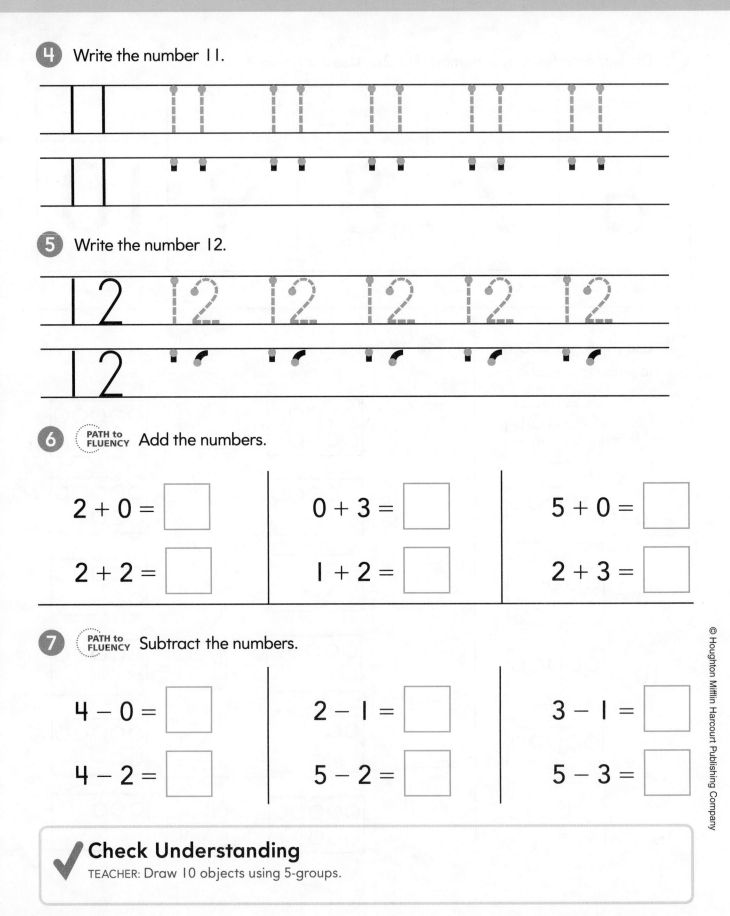

5 Write the number 12.

6 (PATH to FLUENCY) Add the numbers.

2 + 0 = ☐	0 + 3 = ☐	5 + 0 = ☐
2 + 2 = ☐	1 + 2 = ☐	2 + 3 = ☐

7 (PATH to FLUENCY) Subtract the numbers.

4 − 0 = ☐	2 − 1 = ☐	3 − 1 = ☐
4 − 2 = ☐	5 − 2 = ☐	5 − 3 = ☐

✔ **Check Understanding**
TEACHER: Draw 10 objects using 5-groups.

© Houghton Mifflin Harcourt Publishing Company

More Groups of 10

Dear Family:

When children first learn to write numbers, emphasis is placed on forming the numbers correctly. Children begin by tracing, and then are provided with starting points for their pencils. Learning the correct technique helps children learn to write numbers neatly and consistently.

After awhile, children no longer need these hints and are able to write without guide lines or starting points. It is easier for many children to write smaller figures, since they have greater control of the writing tool. With practice, children will gain confidence and speed in writing numbers.

In Unit 3, children continue to practice writing numbers, including 2-digit numbers from 11 to 20. They are already familiar with the individual numbers they will be using. When writing 2-digit numbers, children learn the proper placement and spacing between numbers. The numbers should not be too close together or too far apart, but just the right distance to be read and understood.

Please help and encourage your child as he or she learns to write numbers. This will take time and practice.

Thank you!

Sincerely,
Your child's teacher

Estimada familia:

Cuando los niños aprenden a escribir los números, se enfatiza que deben trazarlos correctamente. Se comienza calcando y luego, se les proporcionan puntos desde donde deben comenzar con sus lápices. Aprender la técnica exacta les servirá a los niños para escribir consistentemente los números de manera correcta.

Después de un tiempo, ya no necesitan estas pistas y pueden escribir sin líneas que les guíen y sin puntos donde comenzar. Es más fácil para muchos niños trazar números pequeños, ya que así tienen más control del instrumento de escritura. Con práctica, los niños adquirirán confianza y velocidad para escribir los números.

En la Unidad 3, los niños continúan practicando la escritura de números, incluyendo los números de 2 dígitos del 11 al 20. Ya están familiarizados con los números individuales que estarán usando. Al escribir números de 2 dígitos, deben aprender su colocación correcta y la distancia correcta que debe haber entre los dígitos. No deben estar demasiado juntos ni demasiado separados, la distancia debe ser adecuada para poder leerlos y comprenderlos.

Por favor ayude a su niño a escribir los números. Esto requerirá tiempo y práctica. Anímelo y apóyelo durante el aprendizaje.

¡Gracias!

Atentamente,
El maestro de su niño

Model Partners Through 6 with Counters

Name _____

1 Write the number 13.

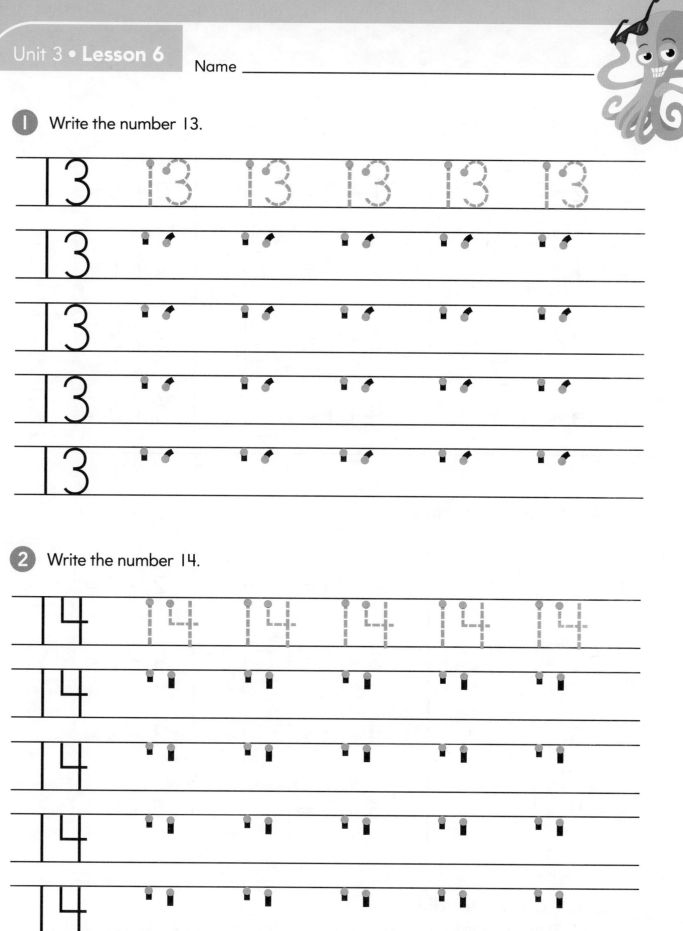

2 Write the number 14.

Model Partners Through 6 with Counters **159**

3 PATH to FLUENCY Add the numbers.

$0 + 2 = \boxed{}$ $1 + 0 = \boxed{}$ $0 + 5 = \boxed{}$

$3 + 1 = \boxed{}$ $1 + 3 = \boxed{}$ $0 + 1 = \boxed{}$

$2 + 3 = \boxed{}$ $2 + 1 = \boxed{}$ $3 + 2 = \boxed{}$

$0 + 4 = \boxed{}$ $4 + 1 = \boxed{}$ $5 + 0 = \boxed{}$

4 PATH to FLUENCY Subtract the numbers.

$1 - 0 = \boxed{}$ $4 - 0 = \boxed{}$ $2 - 0 = \boxed{}$

$5 - 1 = \boxed{}$ $3 - 1 = \boxed{}$ $4 - 1 = \boxed{}$

$5 - 3 = \boxed{}$ $4 - 3 = \boxed{}$ $3 - 3 = \boxed{}$

$4 - 4 = \boxed{}$ $5 - 5 = \boxed{}$ $5 - 4 = \boxed{}$

✓ Check Understanding

TEACHER: Draw 4 dots and a Break-Apart Stick. Then write a matching equation below.

Model Partners Through 6 with Counters

Name _____

1 Draw the circles on the Number Parade. Use a 5-group.

6	7	8	9	10

2 Use the 5-group. Draw to show the number.

6 = ⬜ ○○○○○

7 = ⬜ ○○○○○

8 = ⬜ ○○○○○

9 = ⬜ ○○○○○

10 = ⬜ ○○○○○

3 Write the number.

⬜ = ○○○

⬜ = ○○○○○ ○○

⬜ = ○○○○○ ○○○○

⬜ = ○○○○○ ○

⬜ = ○○

⬜ = ○○○○○ ○○

⬜ = ○○○○○ ○○○

⬜ = ○○○○

⬜ = ○○○○○ ○

⬜ = ○○○○○ ○○○○

⬜ = ○○○○○ ○○○○○

⬜ = ○○○○○

More Addition and Subtraction Stories: Park Scene **161**

4 Write the number 15.

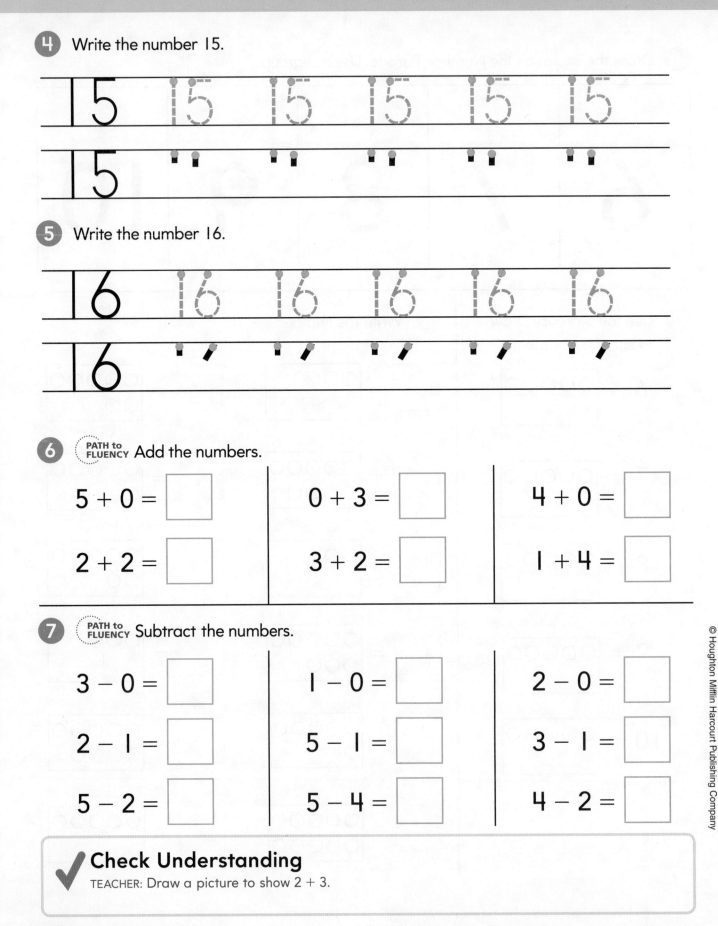

5 Write the number 16.

6 PATH to FLUENCY **Add the numbers.**

$5 + 0 = \boxed{}$ $0 + 3 = \boxed{}$ $4 + 0 = \boxed{}$

$2 + 2 = \boxed{}$ $3 + 2 = \boxed{}$ $1 + 4 = \boxed{}$

7 PATH to FLUENCY **Subtract the numbers.**

$3 - 0 = \boxed{}$ $1 - 0 = \boxed{}$ $2 - 0 = \boxed{}$

$2 - 1 = \boxed{}$ $5 - 1 = \boxed{}$ $3 - 1 = \boxed{}$

$5 - 2 = \boxed{}$ $5 - 4 = \boxed{}$ $4 - 2 = \boxed{}$

✔ **Check Understanding**
TEACHER: Draw a picture to show 2 + 3.

More Addition and Subtraction Stories: Park Scene

Name _____

Use a 10-group.

Write the partners.

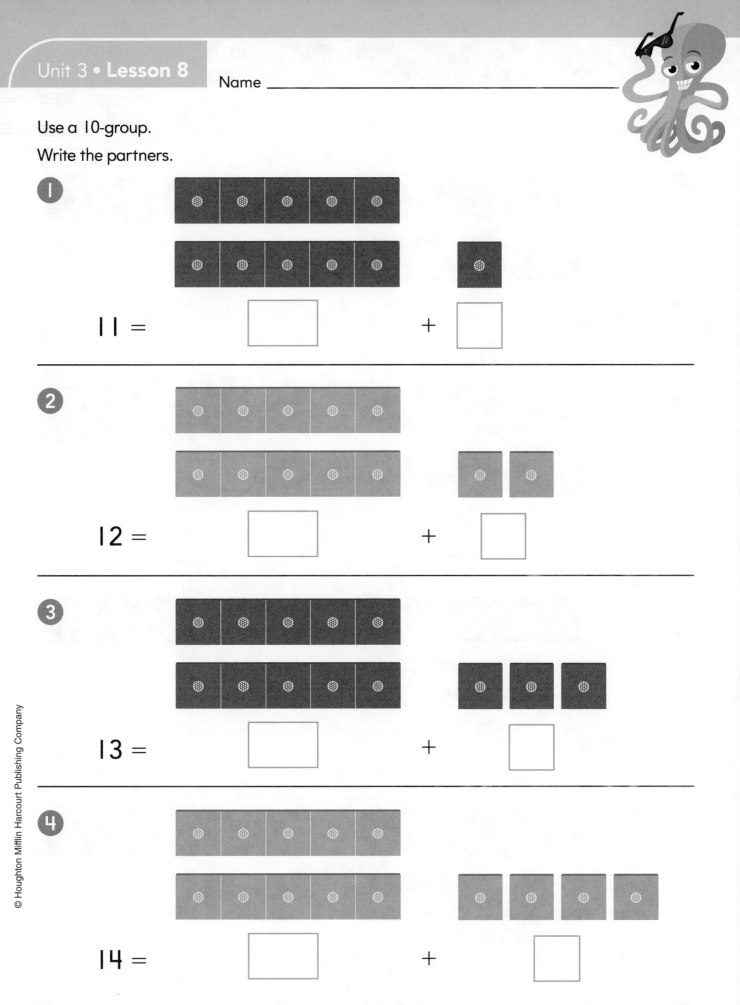

1

11 = ☐ + ☐

2

12 = ☐ + ☐

3

13 = ☐ + ☐

4

14 = ☐ + ☐

Show Tens and Ones **163**

Use a 10-group.

Write the partners.

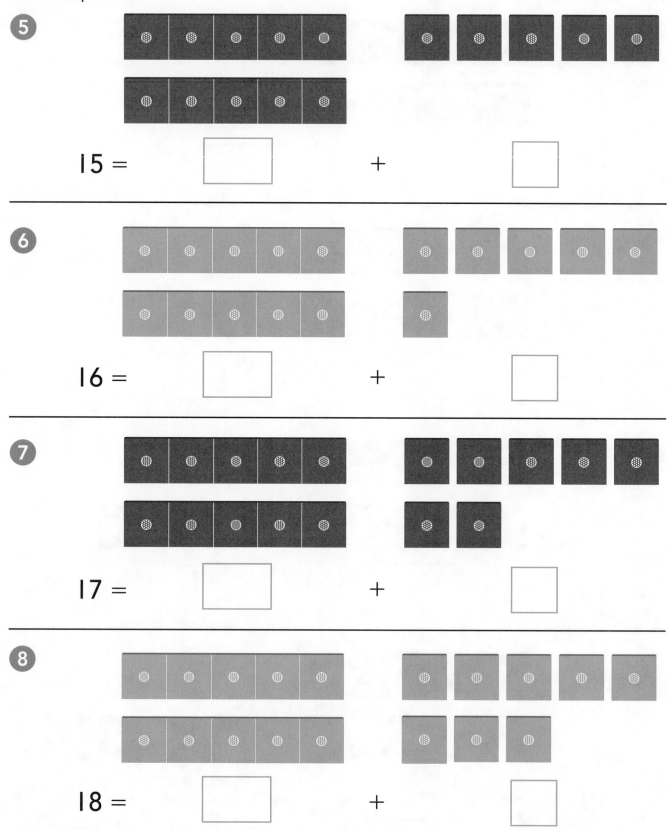

5

15 = ☐ + ☐

6

16 = ☐ + ☐

7

17 = ☐ + ☐

8

18 = ☐ + ☐

Show Tens and Ones

Cut on dashed lines. Fold on solid lines and tape at top and bottom.

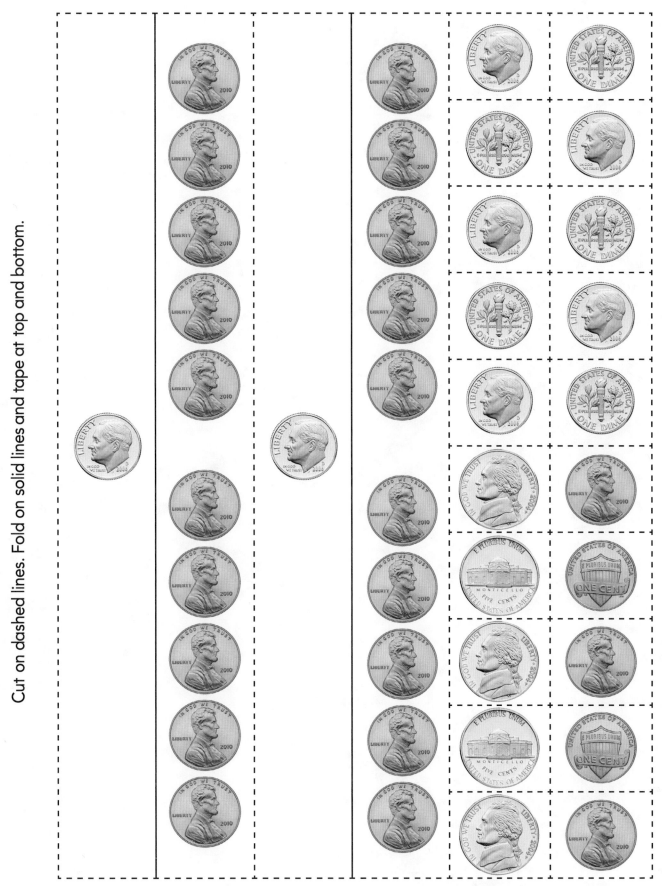

Dime Strips, Dimes, Nickels, Pennies **165**

Dime Strips, Dimes, Nickels, Pennies

Name _____

A **dime** is worth 10¢.

9 Write the number of cents.

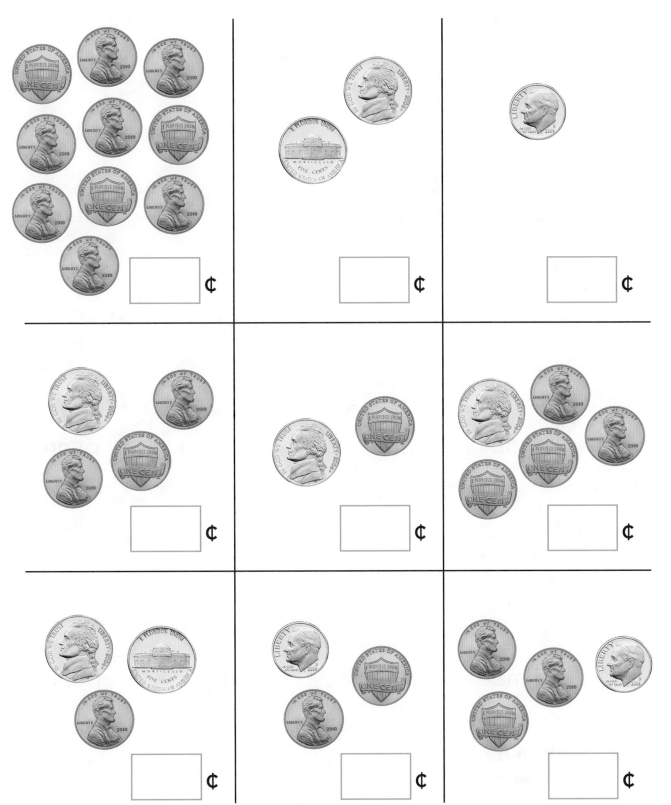

⑩ Use a dime and some pennies.
Draw to show the coins.
Write the number of coins.

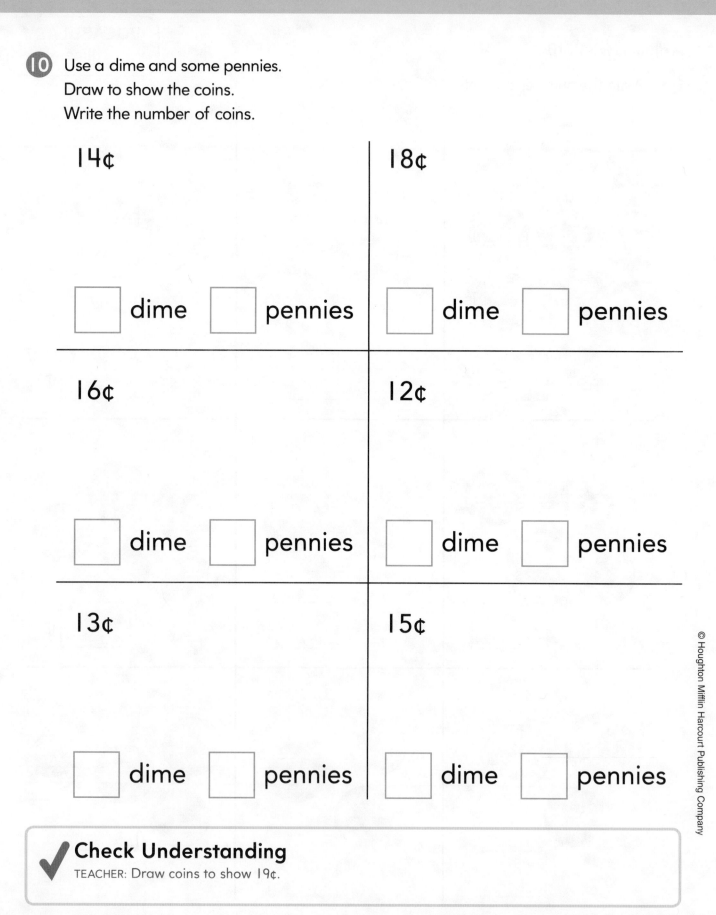

14¢

☐ dime ☐ pennies

18¢

☐ dime ☐ pennies

16¢

☐ dime ☐ pennies

12¢

☐ dime ☐ pennies

13¢

☐ dime ☐ pennies

15¢

☐ dime ☐ pennies

✓ **Check Understanding**
TEACHER: Draw coins to show 19¢.

Show Tens and Ones

Name _____

Build the shape.

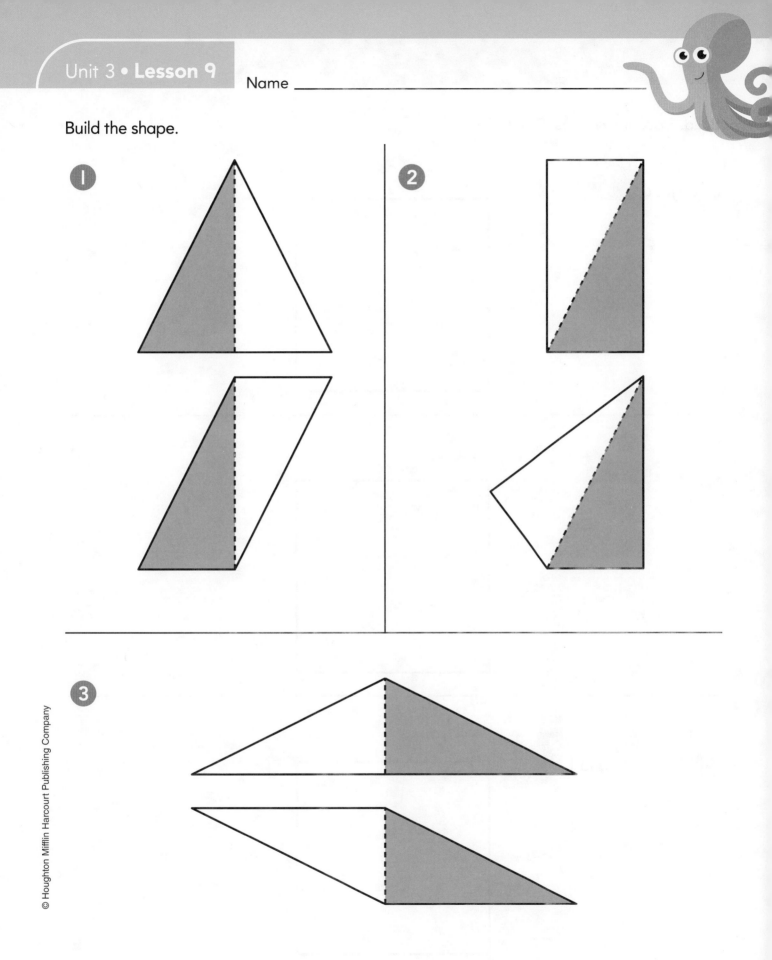

Build. Trace the shapes. Color.

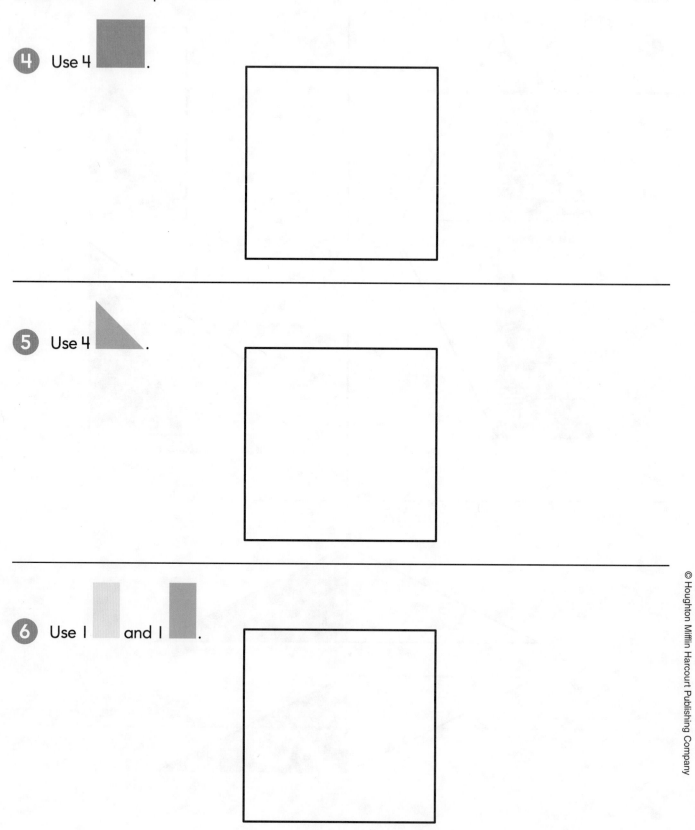

4 Use 4 ⬛ .

5 Use 4 ◺ .

6 Use 1 ▮ and 1 ▮ .

Make New Shapes

Name _____

Build. Trace the shapes. Color.

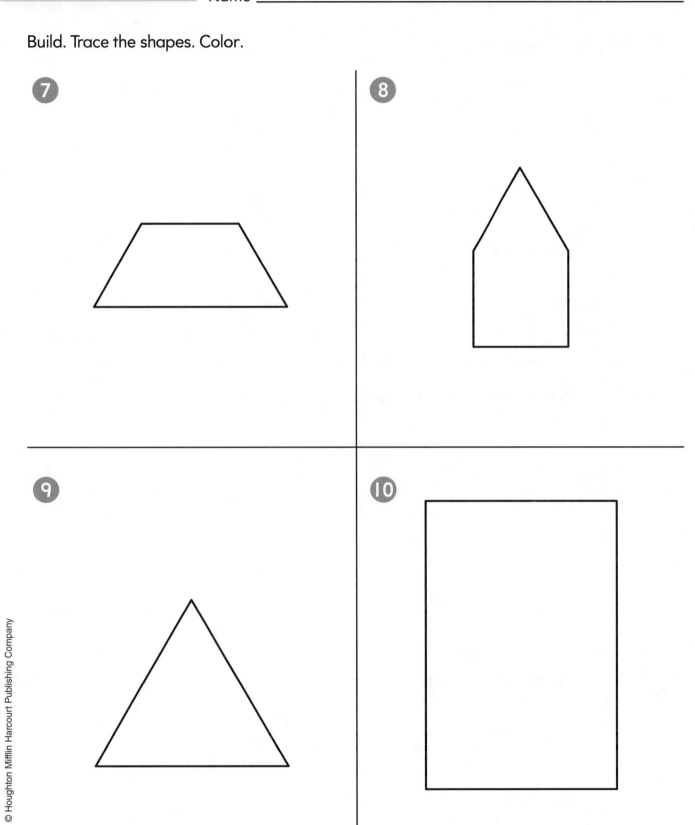

7

8

9

10

Build. Trace the shapes. Color.

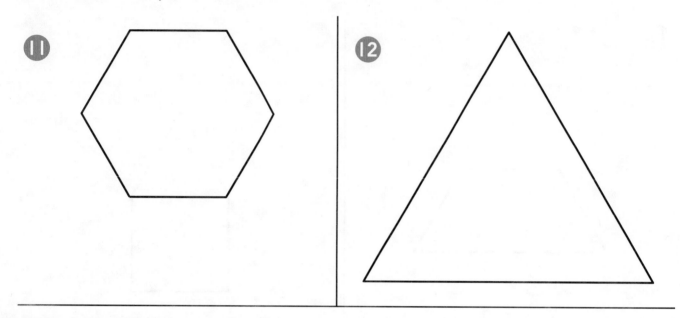

Build a shape. Trace the outline of the shape.

⑬

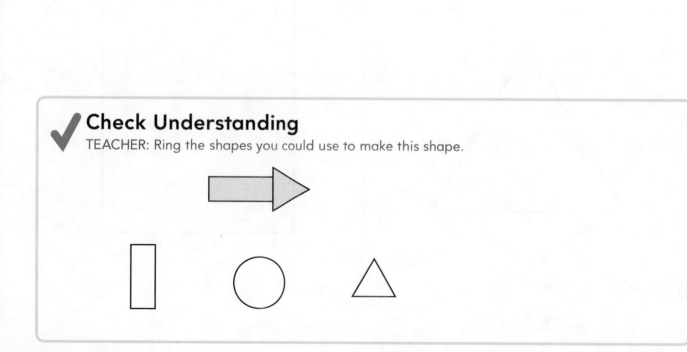

✓ Check Understanding

TEACHER: Ring the shapes you could use to make this shape.

Make New Shapes

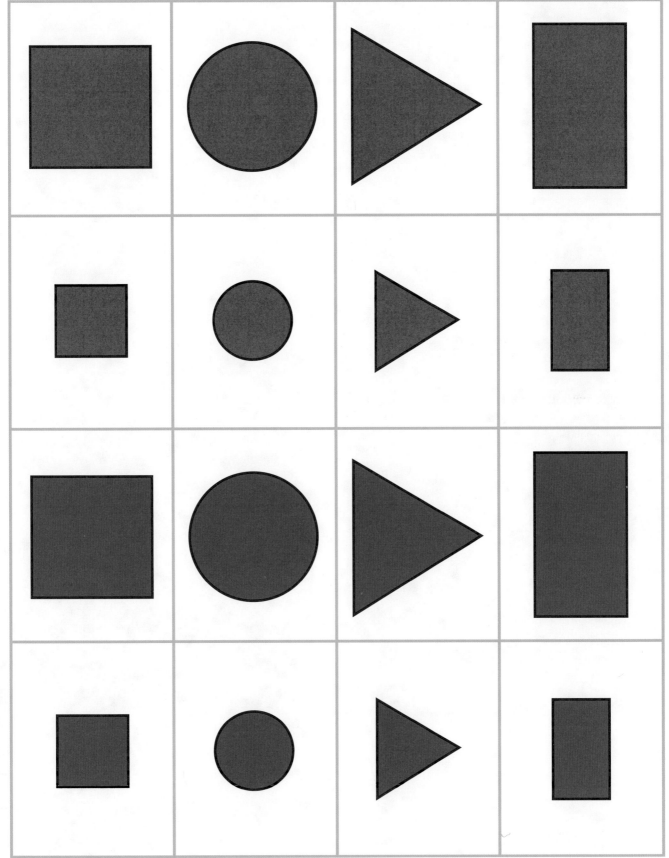

Sorting Cards

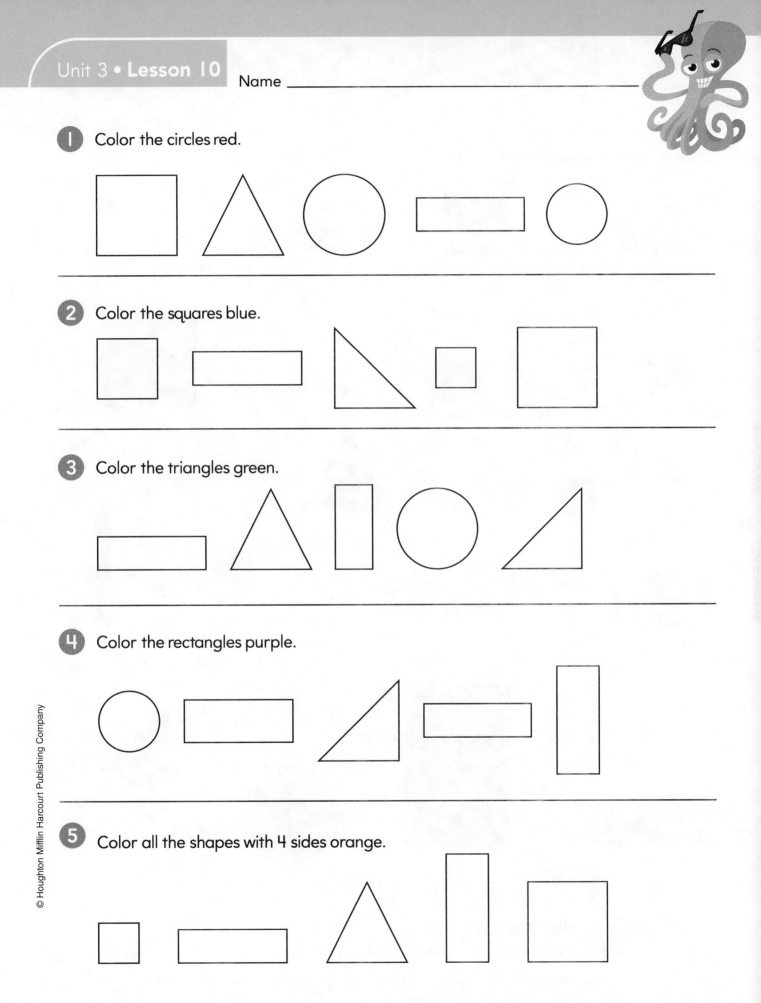

1 Color the circles red.

2 Color the squares blue.

3 Color the triangles green.

4 Color the rectangles purple.

5 Color all the shapes with 4 sides orange.

Ring the squares.

Draw a line under the green shapes.

✔ Check Understanding

TEACHER: Name three different ways objects can be sorted.

Explore Classifying

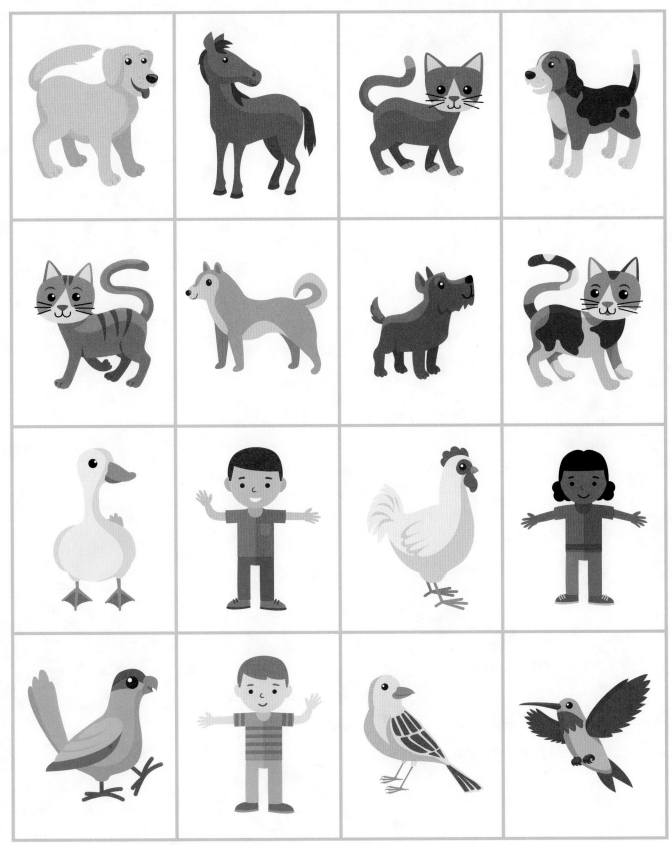

Sorting Cards

1 Draw circles for 1–10.
Show the 5-groups.

1	
2	
3	
4	
5	
6	
7	
8	
9	
10	

2 Use the 5-group. Draw to show the number.

9 = ⃝⃝⃝⃝⃝   7 = ⃝⃝⃝⃝⃝

8 = ⃝⃝⃝⃝⃝   10 = ⃝⃝⃝⃝⃝

6 = ⃝⃝⃝⃝⃝   9 = ⃝⃝⃝⃝⃝

7 = ⃝⃝⃝⃝⃝   8 = ⃝⃝⃝⃝⃝

3 Count how many. Write the number.

☐ ☐ ☐ ☐ ☐

Help Puzzled Penguin.

 Look at Puzzled Penguin's answers.

Am I correct?

 Look at what Puzzled Penguin wrote.

8 fingers

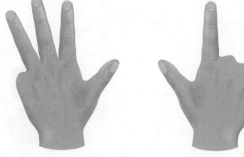

Show $4 + 2$ on your fingers another way.

_____ fingers

 Check Understanding

TEACHER: Tell a story that has a total of 9. Draw a picture to match.

Practice Addition and Subtraction Stories: Park Scene

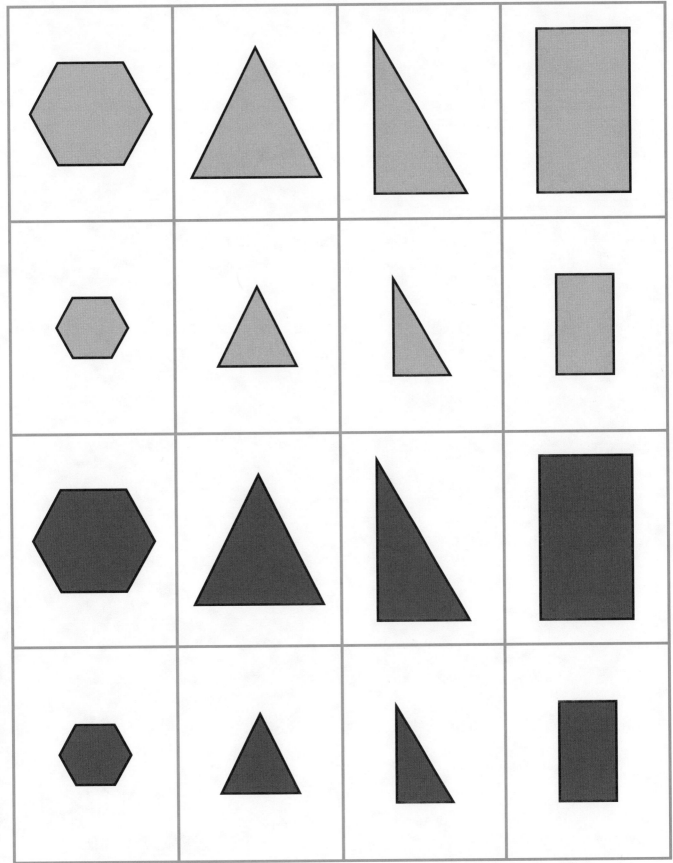

© Houghton Mifflin Harcourt Publishing Company

Sorting Cards

1 Draw circles for 1–10. Show the 5-group.

1	2	3	4	5	6	7	8	9	10
								○○○○○ ○○○○	

2 Write each number and an **equal to sign (=)** or a **not equal to sign (≠)**.

2	≠	4

3 PATH to FLUENCY Add the numbers.

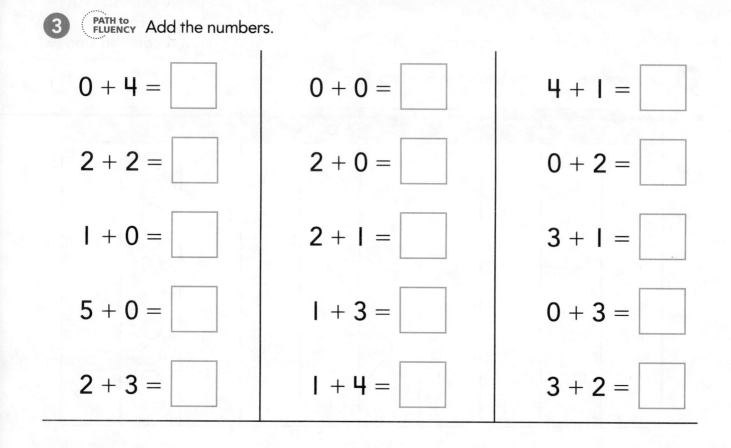

0 + 4 = ☐   0 + 0 = ☐   4 + 1 = ☐

2 + 2 = ☐   2 + 0 = ☐   0 + 2 = ☐

1 + 0 = ☐   2 + 1 = ☐   3 + 1 = ☐

5 + 0 = ☐   1 + 3 = ☐   0 + 3 = ☐

2 + 3 = ☐   1 + 4 = ☐   3 + 2 = ☐

4 PATH to FLUENCY Subtract the numbers.

0 − 0 = ☐   1 − 0 = ☐   4 − 0 = ☐

5 − 2 = ☐   3 − 2 = ☐   2 − 1 = ☐

4 − 4 = ☐   4 − 2 = ☐   5 − 1 = ☐

4 − 3 = ☐   5 − 3 = ☐   3 − 3 = ☐

3 − 1 = ☐   4 − 1 = ☐   2 − 2 = ☐

Practice Classifying

5 Ring the objects that are **alike**.

6 Mark an X on the object that is **different**.

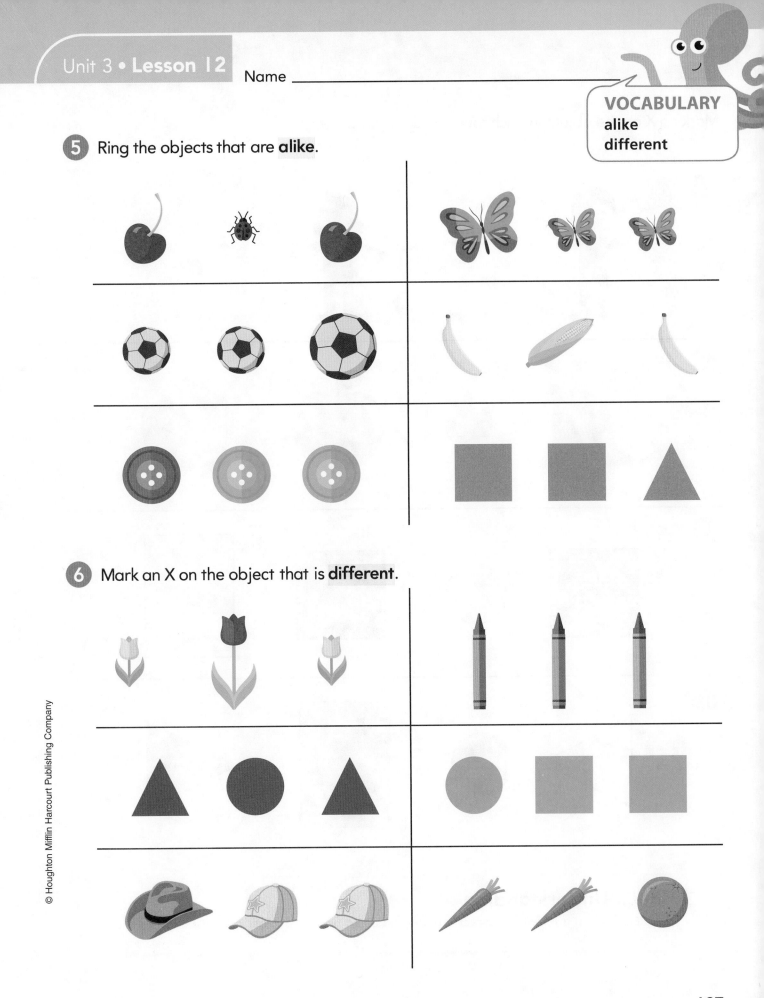

Mark an X on the object in each row that does not belong.

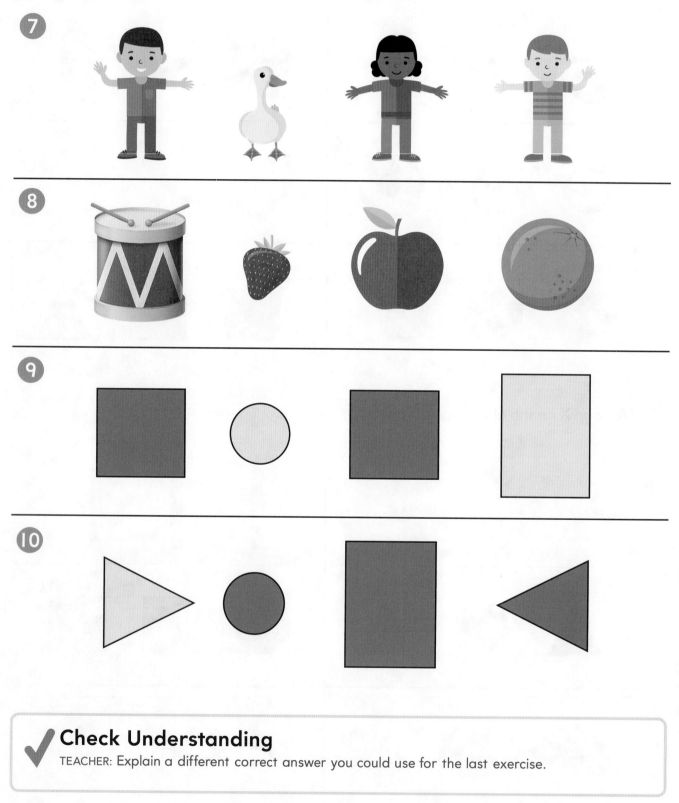

✔ Check Understanding

TEACHER: Explain a different correct answer you could use for the last exercise.

Practice Classifying

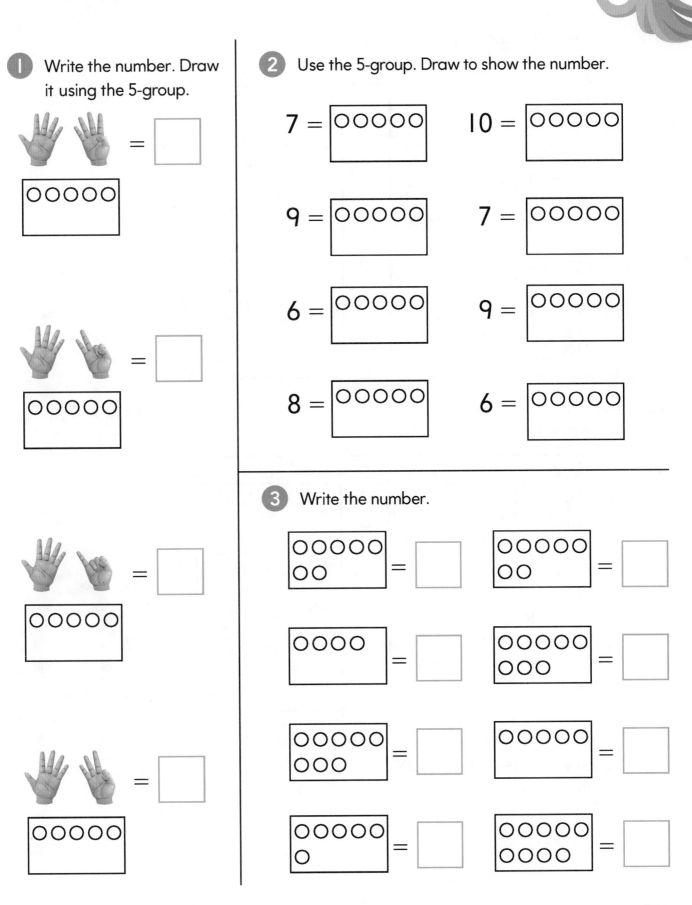

1 Write the number. Draw it using the 5-group.

2 Use the 5-group. Draw to show the number.

7 =

10 =

9 =

7 =

6 =

9 =

8 =

6 =

3 Write the number.

4 Draw a ring around every 5-group.
Write the numbers shown by the circles.

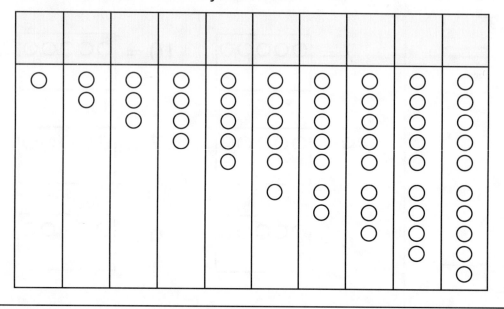

5 Look at what Puzzled Penguin drew.
Help Puzzled Penguin.

Am I correct?

✓ Check Understanding

TEACHER: Explain why you can use two 5-Square Tiles instead of 10 Square-Inch Tiles to show a group of 10.

Build Teen Numbers

Name _____

1 Draw circles for 1–10. Show the 5-group.

1	2	3	4	5	6	7	8	9	10
							○○○○○○○○		

2 Write each number and an equal to sign (=) or a not equal to sign (≠).

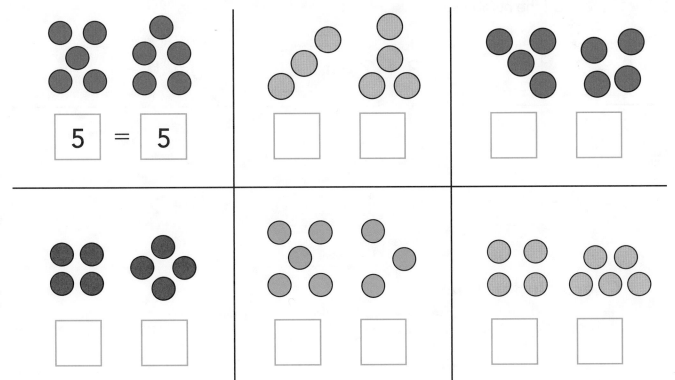

$5 = 5$

Practice with 5-Groups **191**

3 Write the number 15.

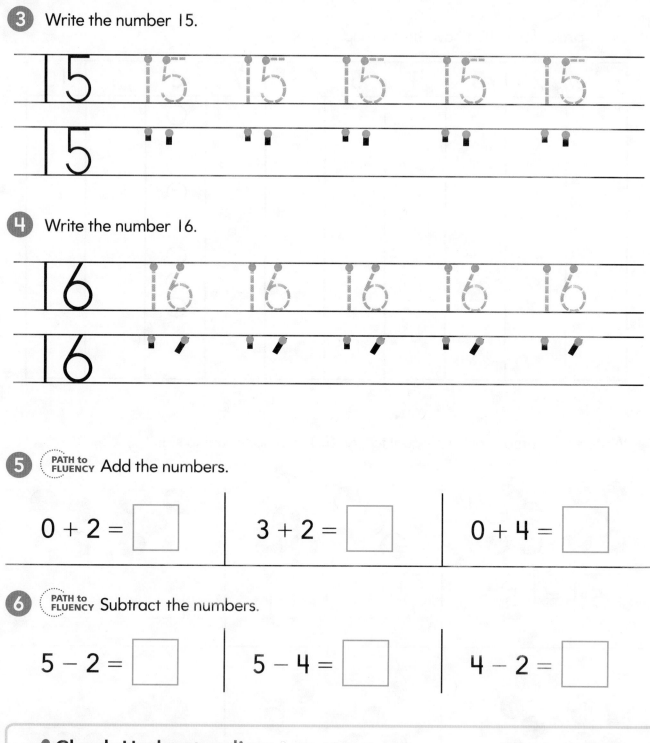

4 Write the number 16.

5 PATH to FLUENCY Add the numbers.

$0 + 2 = \boxed{}$ | $3 + 2 = \boxed{}$ | $0 + 4 = \boxed{}$

6 PATH to FLUENCY Subtract the numbers.

$5 - 2 = \boxed{}$ | $5 - 4 = \boxed{}$ | $4 - 2 = \boxed{}$

✓ **Check Understanding**

TEACHER: Draw 2 groups of objects correctly using the not equal to sign (≠) between them. Then repeat with 2 groups with the equal to sign (=).

Practice with 5-Groups

15

14
10 + 5
10 + 4
19
10 + 9

13
10 + 3
18
10 + 8

12
10 + 2
17
10 + 7

11
10 + 1
16
10 + 6

Teen Total Cards

Name _____

VOCABULARY
teen number

Use a 10-group.

Write the partners.

Write the **teen number**.

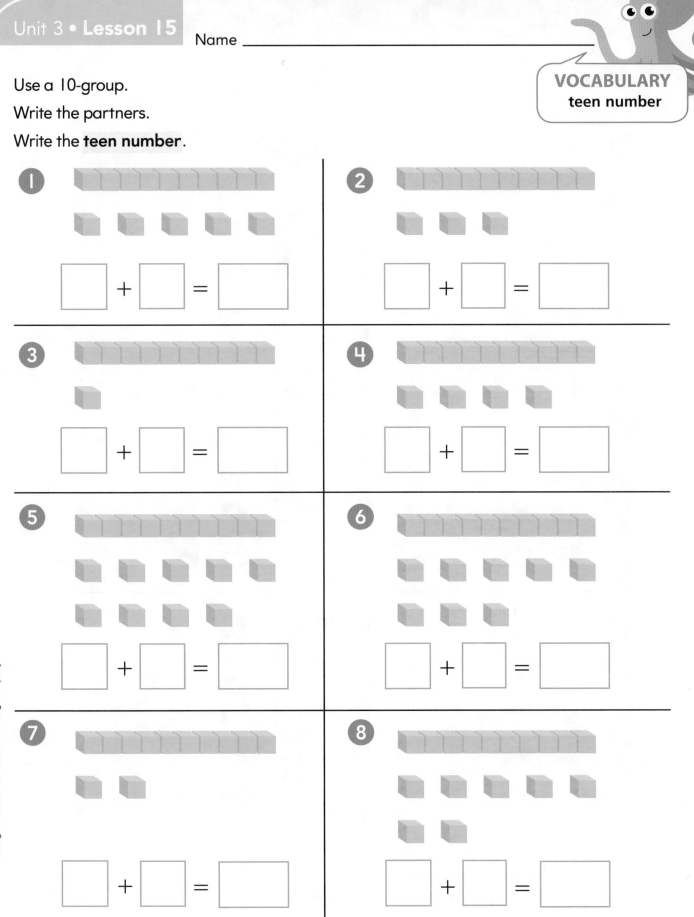

1   ☐ + ☐ = ☐

2   ☐ + ☐ = ☐

3   ☐ + ☐ = ☐

4   ☐ + ☐ = ☐

5   ☐ + ☐ = ☐

6   ☐ + ☐ = ☐

7   ☐ + ☐ = ☐

8   ☐ + ☐ = ☐

Use a 10-group.

Write the teen number.

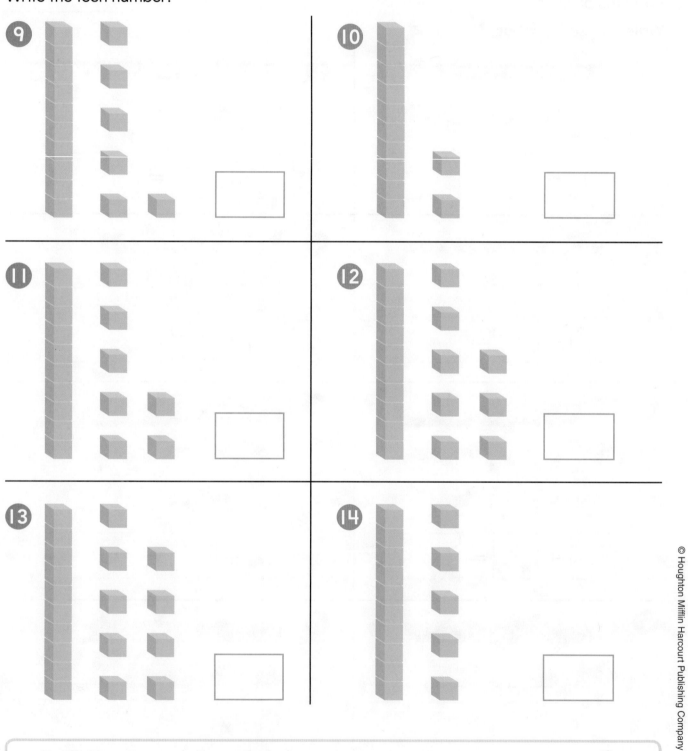

✓ Check Understanding

TEACHER: Draw a 10-group and some extras to show 13.

Tens in Teens

VOCABULARY
unknown

Find partners for 6.

Draw squares to show the **unknown** partner.

Write the partners.

1

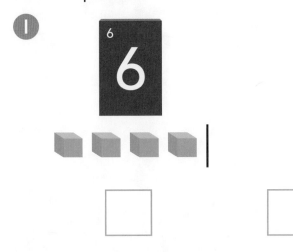

2

3

Find partners for 7.

Draw squares to show the unknown partner.

Write the partners.

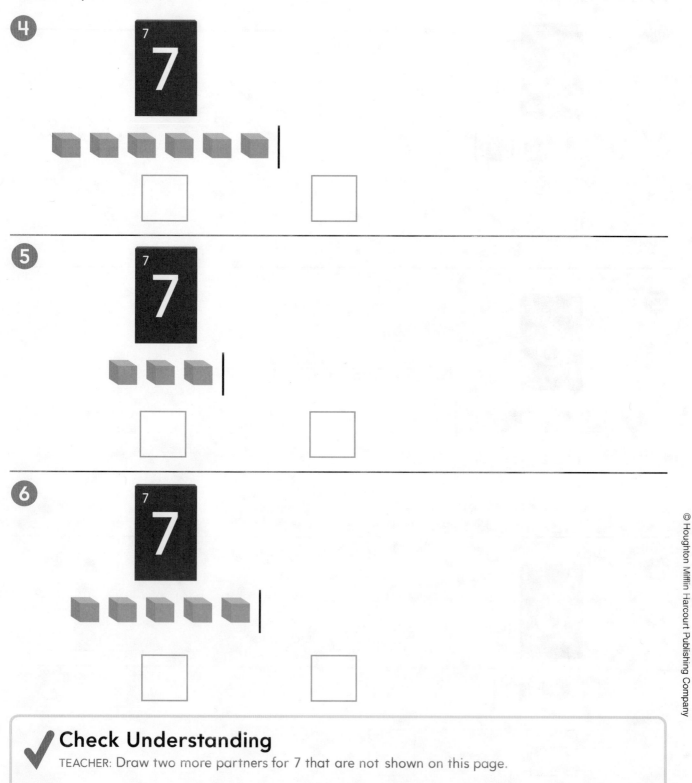

4

7

7

5

7

7

6

7

7

✔ Check Understanding

TEACHER: Draw two more partners for 7 that are not shown on this page.

Stories and Partners

Write the partners.

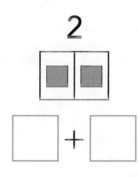

2

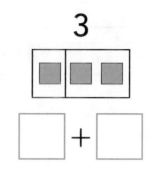

3

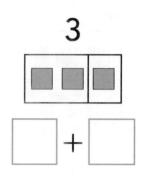

3

☐ + ☐   ☐ + ☐   ☐ + ☐

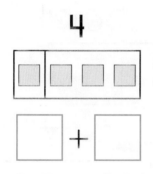

4

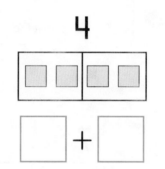

4

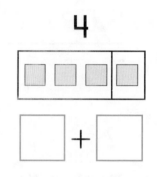

4

☐ + ☐   ☐ + ☐   ☐ + ☐

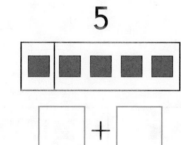

5

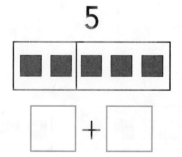

5

☐ + ☐   ☐ + ☐

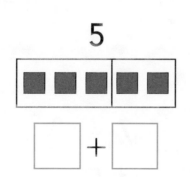

5

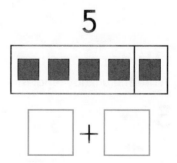

5

☐ + ☐   ☐ + ☐

Write the partners.

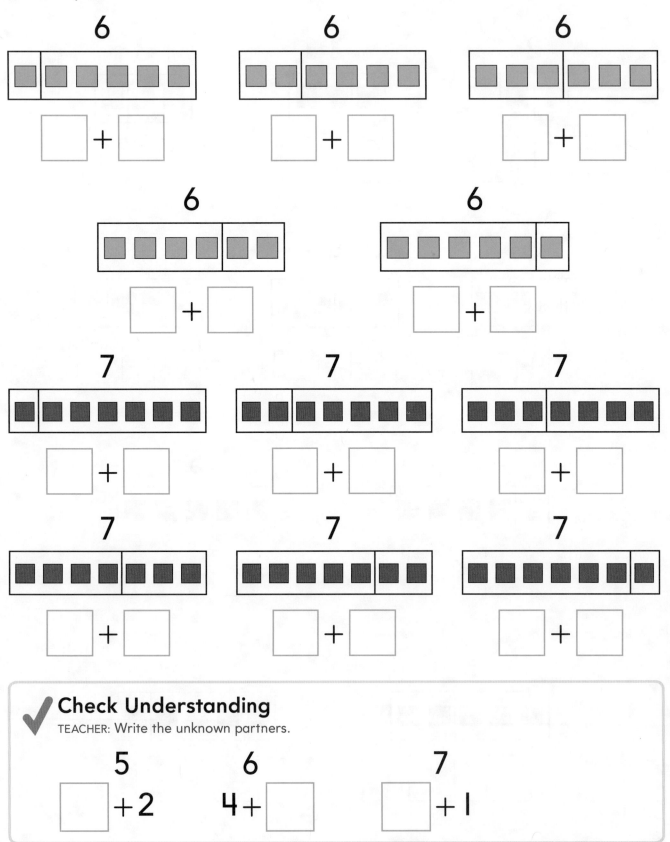

✔ **Check Understanding**

TEACHER: Write the unknown partners.

5

☐ +2

6

4+ ☐

7

☐ +1

Practice with Partners

Dear Family:

In the next few days, please find 20 of the same kind of small object that your child can take to school and paste onto a sheet of paper. For example, your child can use buttons or stickers, or you can cut out 20 small pieces of paper or fabric.

The objects will be used for an activity to help your child learn to see the group of 10 inside each of the teen numbers: 11, 12, 13, 14, 15, 16, 17, 18, and 19.

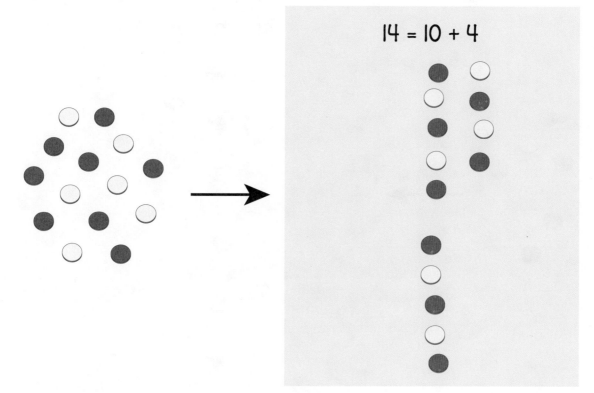

Thank you for your cooperation!

Sincerely,
Your child's teacher

Estimada familia:

Durante los días siguientes, por favor busque 20 objetos pequeños, del mismo tipo, que su niño pueda llevar a la escuela y pegar en una hoja de papel. Por ejemplo, su niño puede usar botones o adhesivos, o usted puede cortar 20 pedacitos de papel o tela.

Los objetos se usarán en una actividad que ayudará a su niño a identificar el grupo de 10 que hay en cada uno de los números de 11 a 19: 11, 12, 13, 14, 15, 16, 17, 18 y 19.

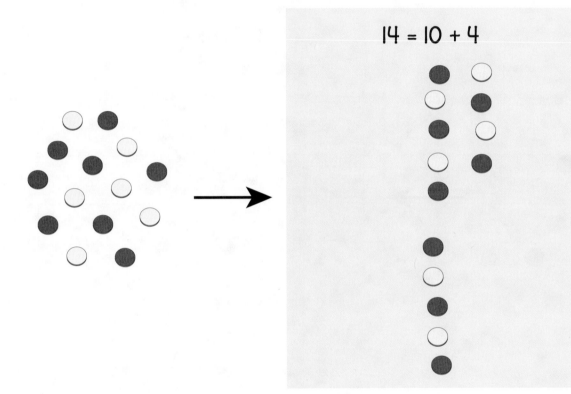

¡Gracias por su colaboración!

Atentamente,
El maestro de su niño

Build Teen Numbers with Classroom Objects

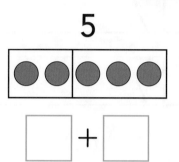

1 Write the partners. Look for switched partners.

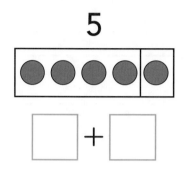 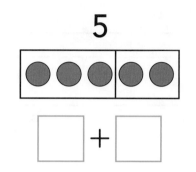

5

☐ + ☐

5

☐ + ☐

5

☐ + ☐

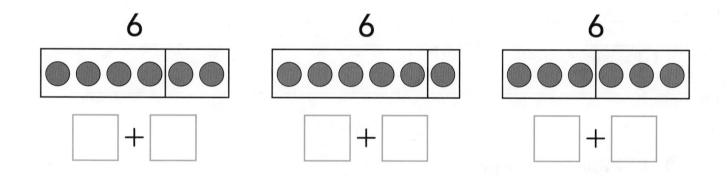

6

☐ + ☐

6

☐ + ☐

6

☐ + ☐

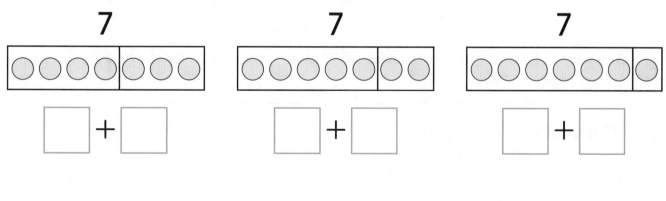

7

☐ + ☐

7

☐ + ☐

7

☐ + ☐

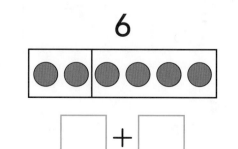 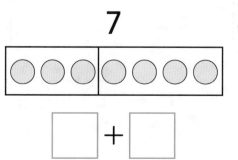

5

☐ + ☐

6

☐ + ☐

7

☐ + ☐

Build Teen Numbers with Classroom Objects **203**

2 Write the number 17.

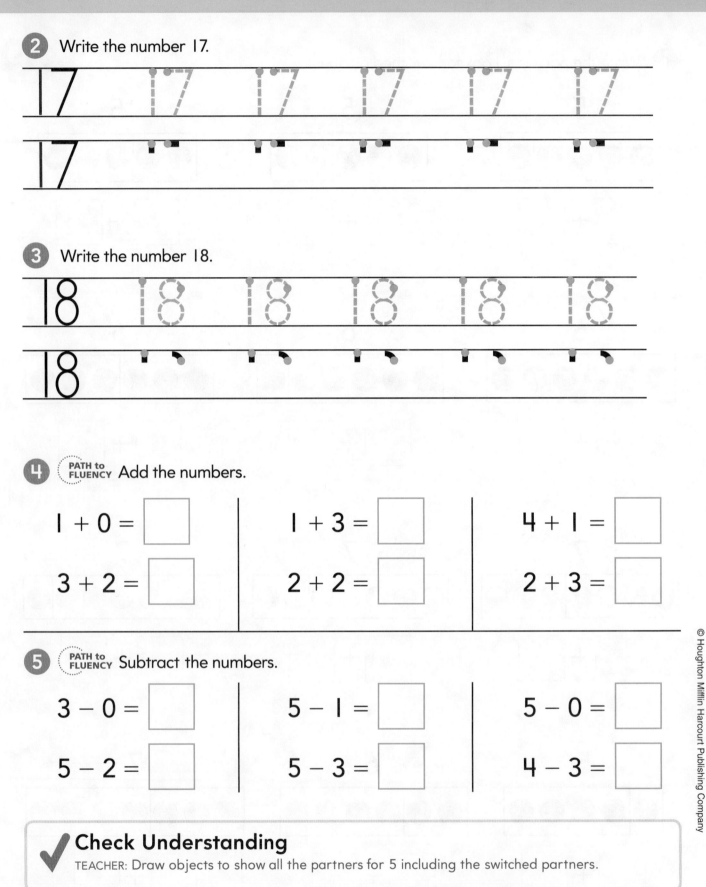

17 17 17 17 17 17

17

3 Write the number 18.

18 18 18 18 18 18

18

4 PATH to FLUENCY Add the numbers.

1 + 0 = ☐   1 + 3 = ☐   4 + 1 = ☐

3 + 2 = ☐   2 + 2 = ☐   2 + 3 = ☐

5 PATH to FLUENCY Subtract the numbers.

3 − 0 = ☐   5 − 1 = ☐   5 − 0 = ☐

5 − 2 = ☐   5 − 3 = ☐   4 − 3 = ☐

✓ **Check Understanding**
TEACHER: Draw objects to show all the partners for 5 including the switched partners.

Build Teen Numbers with Classroom Objects

1 Puzzled Penguin showed the partners
for two teen numbers and wrote the total.
Help Puzzled Penguin.

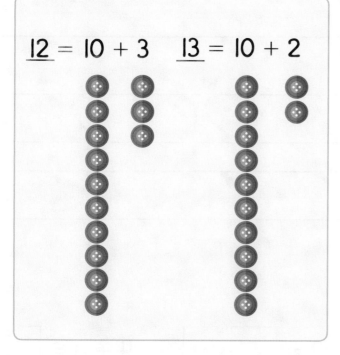

$\underline{12} = 10 + 3$ $\underline{13} = 10 + 2$

Am I correct?

2 Draw the buttons. Write the total.

$\underline{} = 10 + 5$ $\underline{} = 10 + 1$

3 Write the number 19.

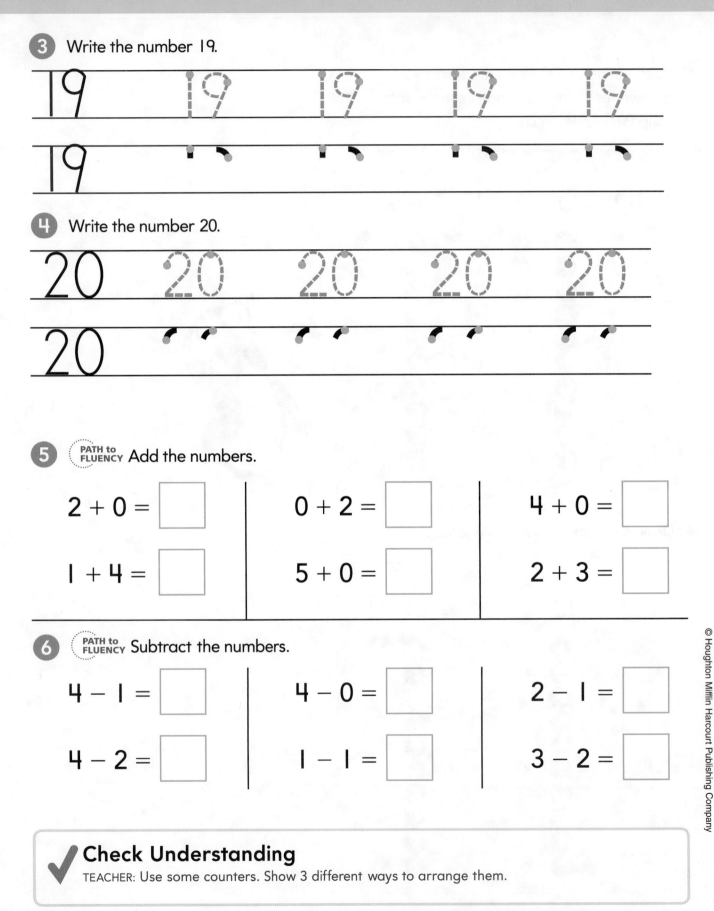

19 19 19 19 19

19

4 Write the number 20.

20 20 20 20 20

20

5 PATH to FLUENCY Add the numbers.

2 + 0 = ☐   0 + 2 = ☐   4 + 0 = ☐

1 + 4 = ☐   5 + 0 = ☐   2 + 3 = ☐

6 PATH to FLUENCY Subtract the numbers.

4 – 1 = ☐   4 – 0 = ☐   2 – 1 = ☐

4 – 2 = ☐   1 – 1 = ☐   3 – 2 = ☐

✓ **Check Understanding**

TEACHER: Use some counters. Show 3 different ways to arrange them.

Show Teen Numbers with Classroom Objects

Name _____

Write the partners for each teen number.

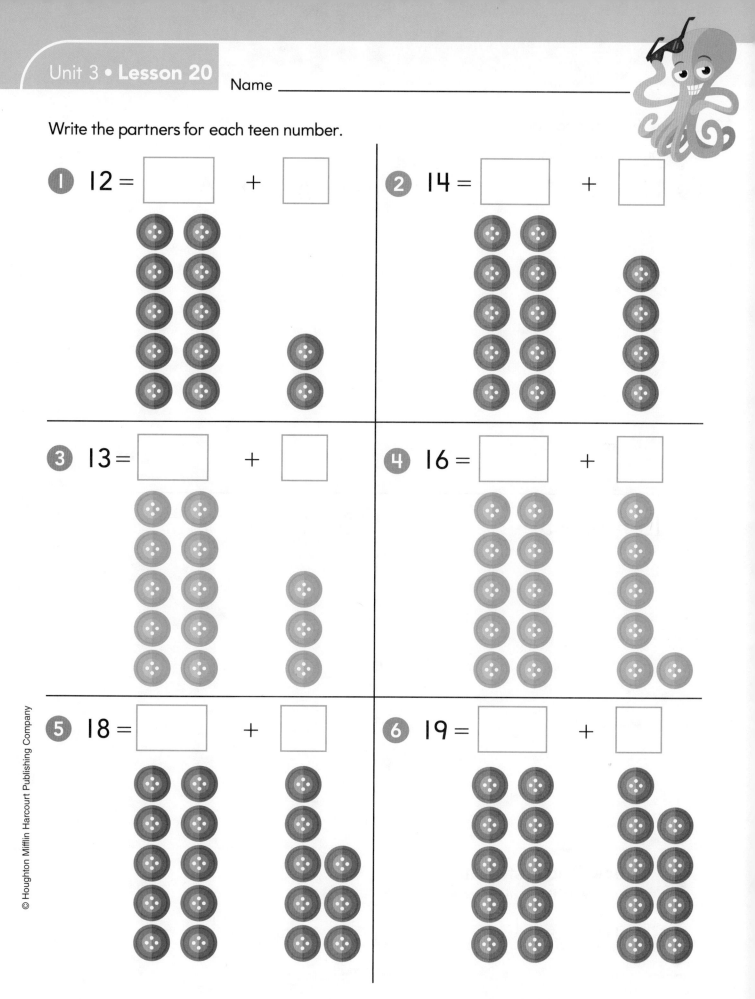

1 12 = ☐ + ☐

2 14 = ☐ + ☐

3 13 = ☐ + ☐

4 16 = ☐ + ☐

5 18 = ☐ + ☐

6 19 = ☐ + ☐

Object Collections: Teen Numbers **207**

Look at the total and partners.

Draw buttons to match.

7 $11 = 10 + 1$

8 $16 = 10 + 6$

9 $15 = 10 + 5$

10 $17 = 10 + 7$

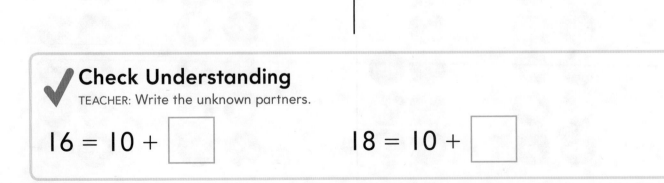

✔ Check Understanding

TEACHER: Write the unknown partners.

$16 = 10 +$ ▢

$18 = 10 +$ ▢

Object Collections: Teen Numbers

Color all the shapes of one kind the color shown below.

Count the number of each shape in the picture. Write the number.

Draw your own smiling faces!

square	rectangle	circle	triangle	hexagon

Ring the picture that matches the statement.

VOCABULARY
below   beside
behind   next to
between

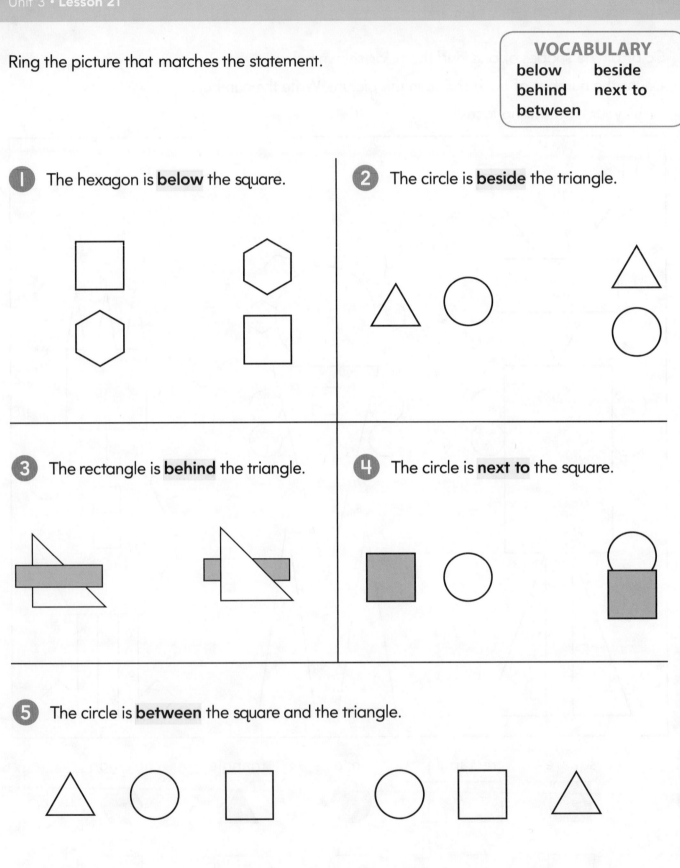

1 The hexagon is **below** the square.

2 The circle is **beside** the triangle.

3 The rectangle is **behind** the triangle.

4 The circle is **next to** the square.

5 The circle is **between** the square and the triangle.

Focus on Problem Solving

1 Write the partners.

6

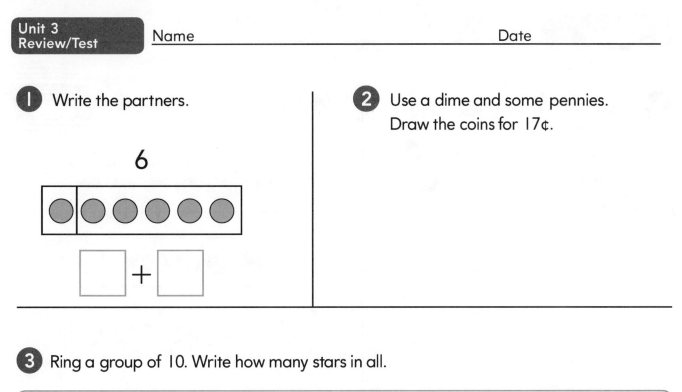

☐ + ☐

2 Use a dime and some pennies.
Draw the coins for 17¢.

3 Ring a group of 10. Write how many stars in all.

4 Ring the number. Draw that number using a 5-group.

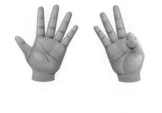

6

7

8

○ ○ ○ ○ ○

5 Write each number. Ring = or ≠.

☐   = / ≠   ☐

6 Choose all the partners that are equal to 6.

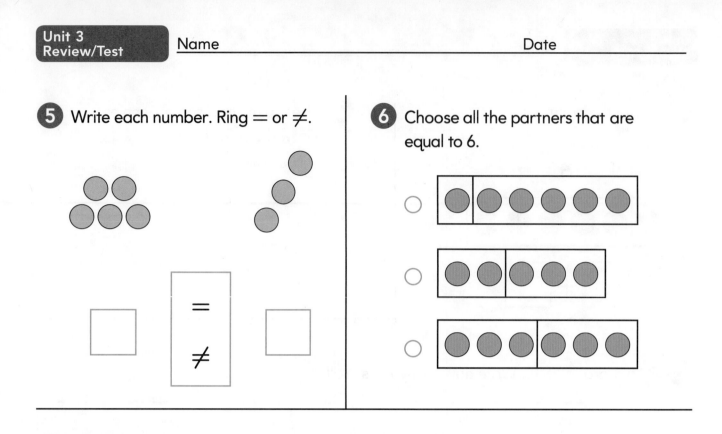

---

7 Add the numbers. Ring the answer.

$3 + 1 = $ ☐

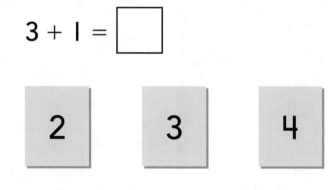

| 2 | 3 | 4 |

---

8 Subtract the numbers. Ring the answer.

$4 - 2 = $ ☐

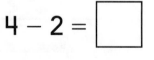

| 2 | 3 | 4 |

Use the picture below to complete Exercises 9–12.

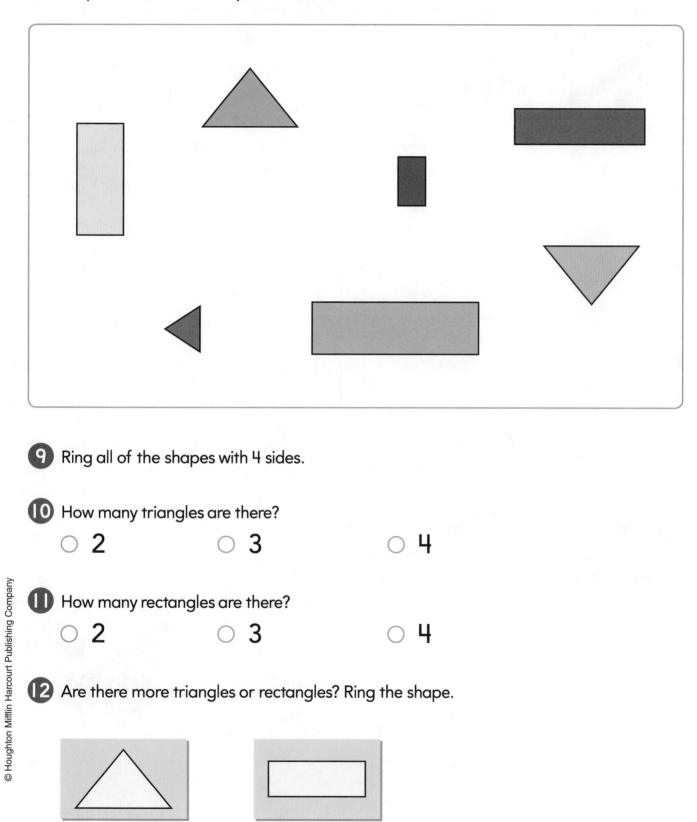

9 Ring all of the shapes with 4 sides.

10 How many triangles are there?

   ○ 2   ○ 3   ○ 4

11 How many rectangles are there?

   ○ 2   ○ 3   ○ 4

12 Are there more triangles or rectangles? Ring the shape.

13 Two triangles are joined. Draw a shape they could make.

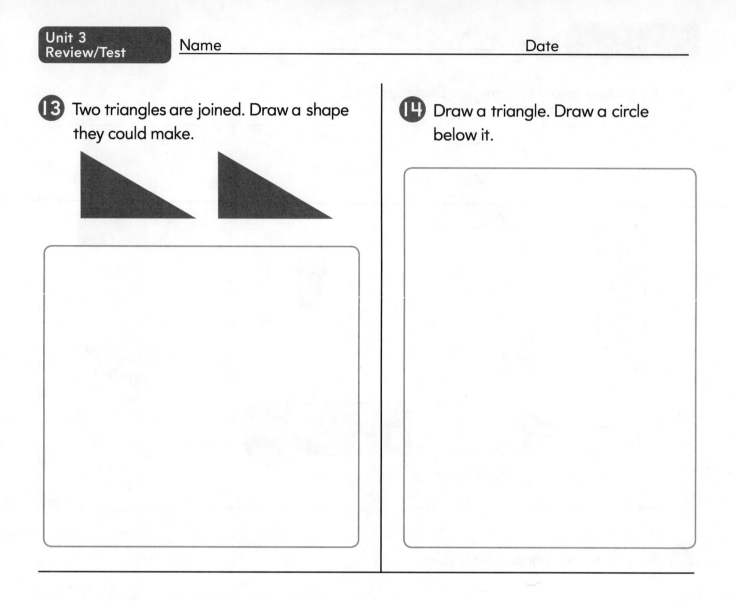

14 Draw a triangle. Draw a circle below it.

15 Draw to show the story problem. Write the answer.
Shane sees 5 butterflies. Tony sees 2 butterflies.
How many butterflies do they see in all?

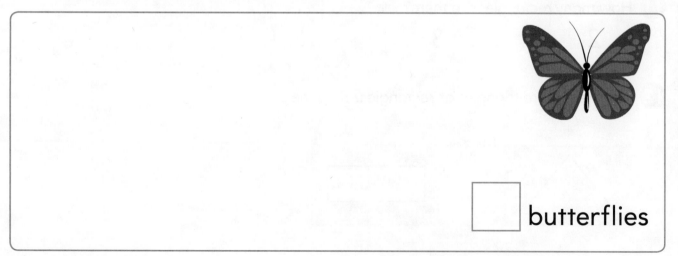

☐ butterflies

Favorite Places

Part A

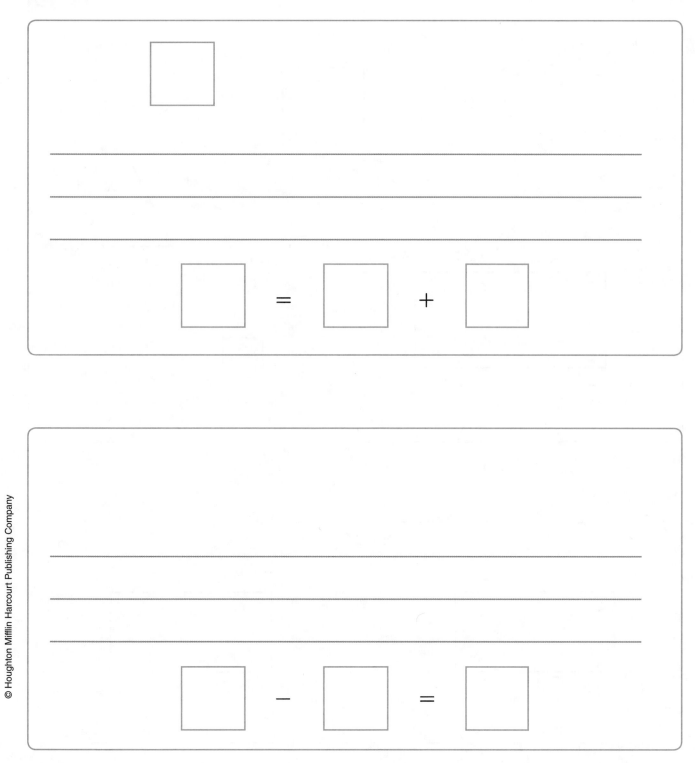

Part B

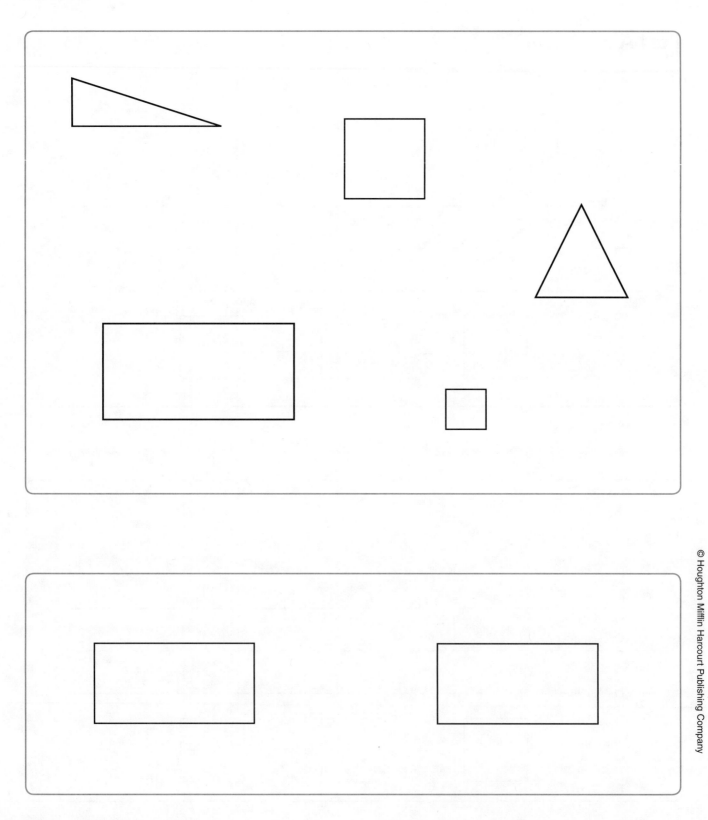

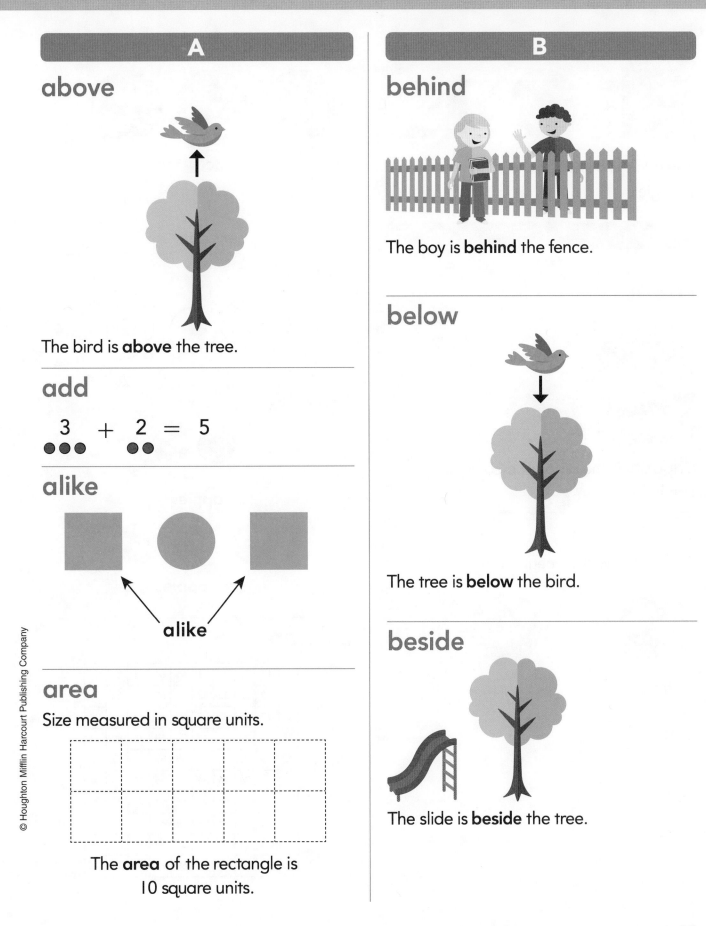

A

above

The bird is **above** the tree.

add

3 + 2 = 5

alike

alike

area

Size measured in square units.

The **area** of the rectangle is
10 square units.

B

behind

The boy is **behind** the fence.

below

The tree is **below** the bird.

beside

The slide is **beside** the tree.

between

The circle is **between** the square and the triangle.

C

capacity

Capacity is the amount a container can hold.

cent

A penny is worth 1 cent, or 1¢.

front   back

cent sign (¢)

3¢

↑

cent sign

circle

classify

apples

not apples

column

1	11	21	31	41	51	61	71	81	91
2	12	22	32	42	52	62	72	82	92
3	13	23	33	43	53	63	73	83	93
4	14	24	34	44	54	64	74	84	94
5	15	25	35	45	55	65	75	85	95
6	16	26	36	46	56	66	76	86	96
7	17	27	37	47	57	67	77	87	97
8	18	28	38	48	58	68	78	88	98
9	19	29	39	49	59	69	79	89	99
10	20	30	40	50	60	70	80	90	100

cone

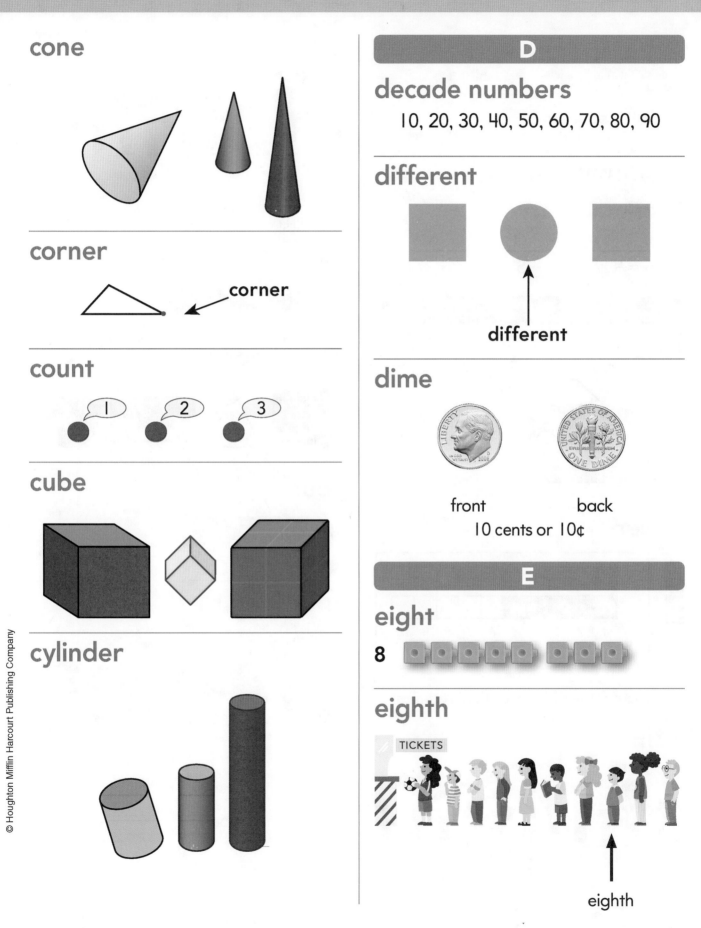

corner

corner

count

1 2 3

cube

cylinder

© Houghton Mifflin Harcourt Publishing Company

D

decade numbers

10, 20, 30, 40, 50, 60, 70, 80, 90

different

different

dime

front   back
10 cents or 10¢

E

eight

8

eighth

TICKETS

eighth

equal to sign (=)

4 + 4 = 8

4 plus 4 is **equal to** 8.

equation

Examples:

4 + 3 = 7   7 = 4 + 3

9 − 5 = 4   4 = 9 − 5

F

face

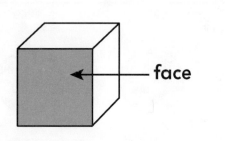

face

fewer

There are **fewer** blue tiles than red tiles.

fifth

fifth

first

first

five

5

flat shapes

four

4

fourth

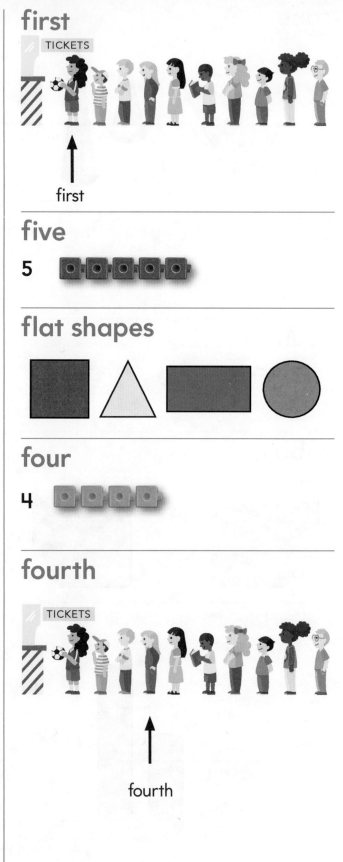

fourth

G

greater

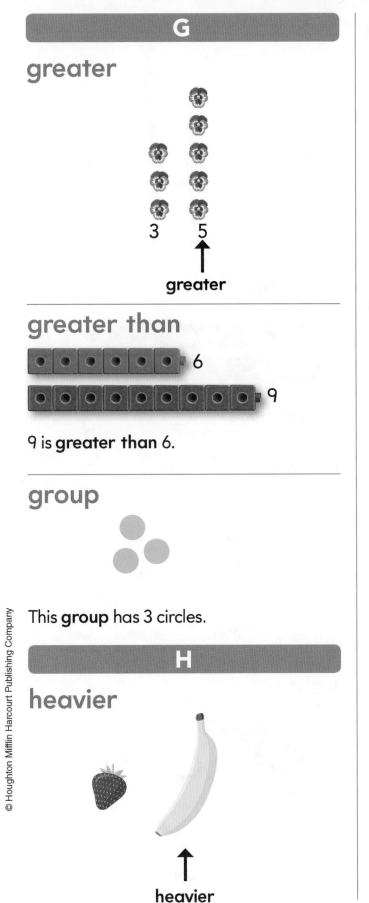

3   5

↑
greater

greater than

9 is **greater than** 6.

group

This **group** has 3 circles.

H

heavier

↑
heavier

heaviest

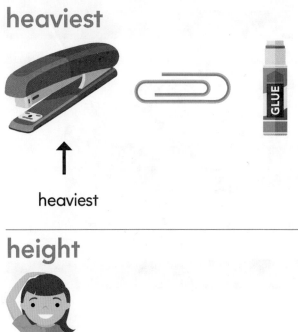

heaviest

height

Height is how tall a person or an object is.

hexagon

how many

Example:

How many fingers? 5 fingers

Glossary

I

in front of

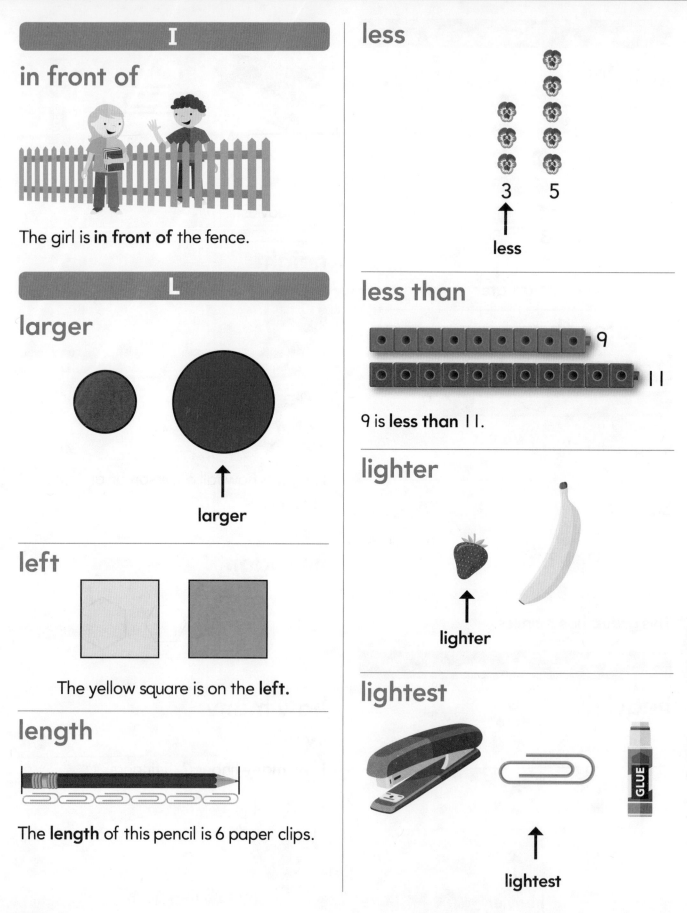

The girl is **in front of** the fence.

L

larger

larger

left

The yellow square is on the **left.**

length

The **length** of this pencil is 6 paper clips.

less

3   5

less

less than

9

11

9 is **less than** 11.

lighter

lighter

lightest

lightest

longer

longer

The pencil is **longer** than the crayon.

longest

longest

M

minus (–)

8 – 3 = 5

8 **minus** 3 equals 5.

more

There are **more** red tiles than blue tiles.

N

next to

The tree is **next to** the slide.

nickel

front   back

5 cents or 5¢

nine

9

ninth

TICKETS

ninth

not equal to sign (≠)

6 ≠ 8

6 is **not equal to** 8.

O

one

I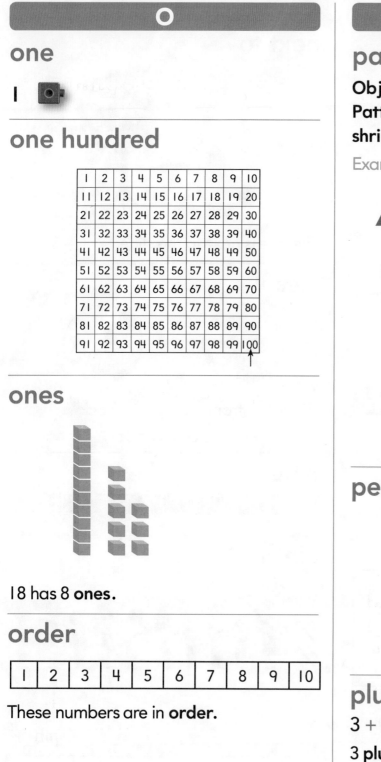

one hundred

1	2	3	4	5	6	7	8	9	10
11	12	13	14	15	16	17	18	19	20
21	22	23	24	25	26	27	28	29	30
31	32	33	34	35	36	37	38	39	40
41	42	43	44	45	46	47	48	49	50
51	52	53	54	55	56	57	58	59	60
61	62	63	64	65	66	67	68	69	70
71	72	73	74	75	76	77	78	79	80
81	82	83	84	85	86	87	88	89	90
91	92	93	94	95	96	97	98	99	100

ones

18 has 8 **ones.**

order

1	2	3	4	5	6	7	8	9	10

These numbers are in **order.**

P

pattern

Objects arranged in a special way. Patterns can be repeating, growing, or shrinking.

Example:

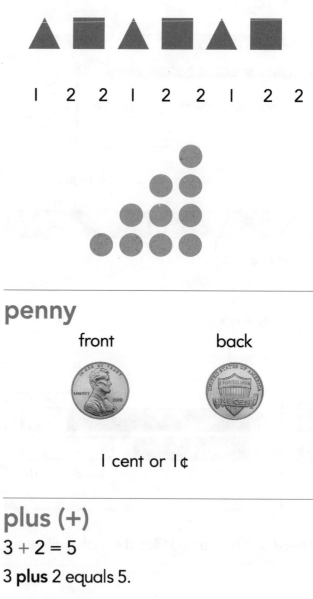

1 2 2 1 2 2 1 2 2

penny

front   back

1 cent or 1¢

plus (+)

3 + 2 = 5

3 **plus** 2 equals 5.

Q

quarter

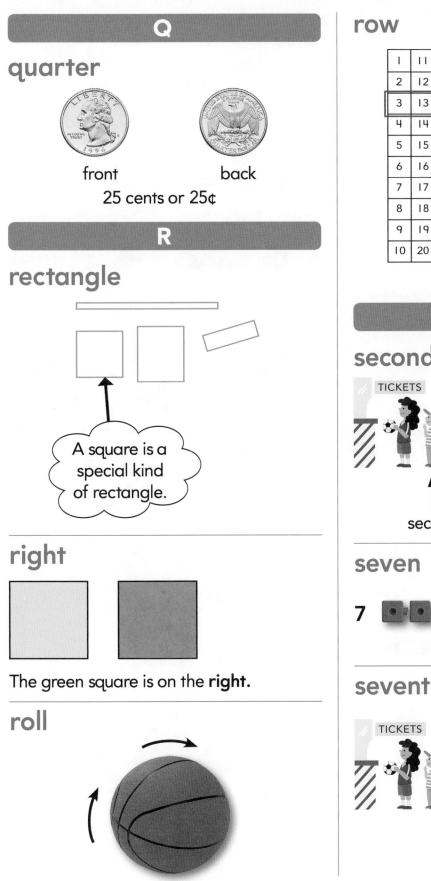

front   back

25 cents or 25¢

R

rectangle

A square is a special kind of rectangle.

right

The green square is on the **right.**

roll

row

1	11	21	31	41	51	61	71	81	91
2	12	22	32	42	52	62	72	82	92
3	13	23	33	43	53	63	73	83	93
4	14	24	34	44	54	64	74	84	94
5	15	25	35	45	55	65	75	85	95
6	16	26	36	46	56	66	76	86	96
7	17	27	37	47	57	67	77	87	97
8	18	28	38	48	58	68	78	88	98
9	19	29	39	49	59	69	79	89	99
10	20	30	40	50	60	70	80	90	100

S

second

second

seven

7

seventh

seventh

Glossary

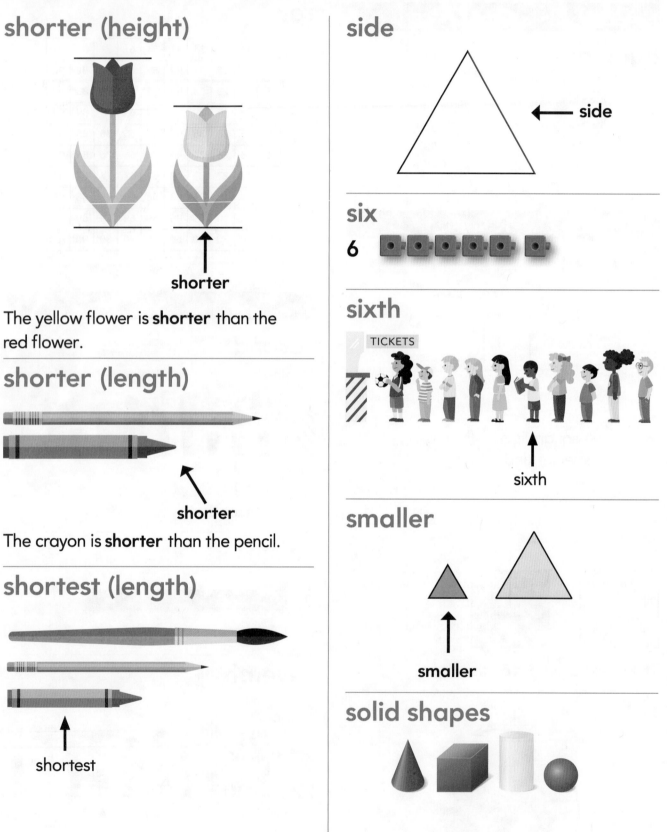

shorter (height)

shorter

The yellow flower is **shorter** than the red flower.

shorter (length)

shorter

The crayon is **shorter** than the pencil.

shortest (length)

shortest

side

← **side**

six
6

sixth

TICKETS

sixth

smaller

smaller

solid shapes

sort

You can **sort** animals into groups.

sphere

square

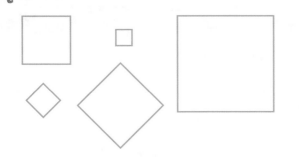

stack

story problem

Example:

There are 2 bunnies in the garden.
Then 3 more bunnies come.
How many bunnies are there in total?

straight lines

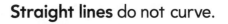

Straight lines do not curve.

subtract

$8 - 3 = 5$

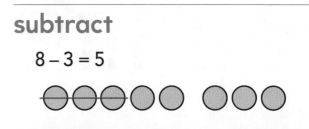

T

taller

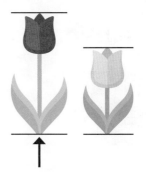

taller

The red flower is **taller** than the yellow flower.

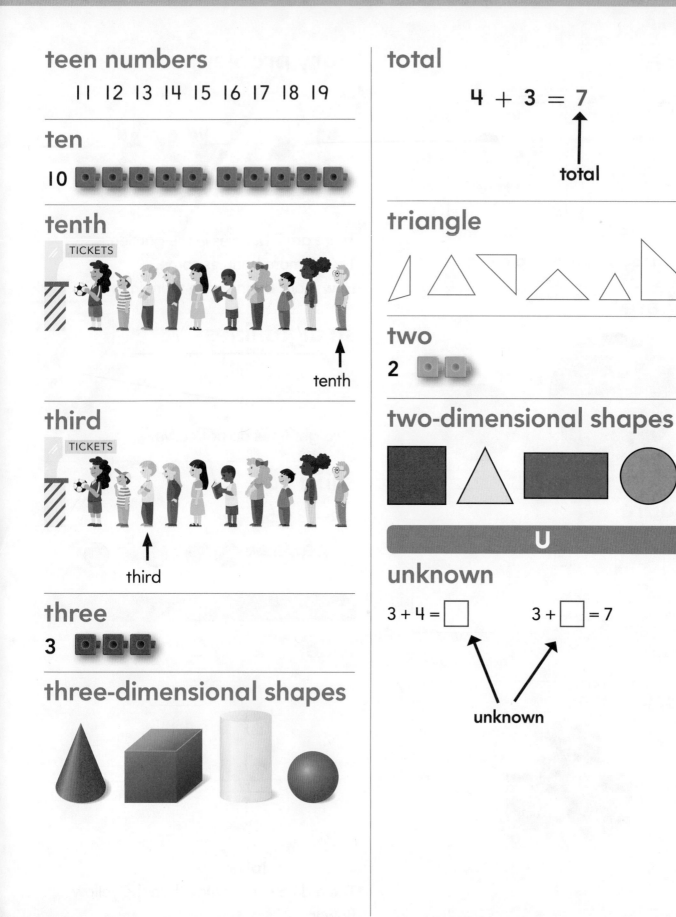

teen numbers

11 12 13 14 15 16 17 18 19

ten

10

tenth

TICKETS

tenth

third

TICKETS

third

three

3

three-dimensional shapes

total

$$4 + 3 = 7$$

total

triangle

two

2

two-dimensional shapes

U

unknown

$3 + 4 = \square$ $3 + \square = 7$

unknown

W

weight

Weight is how heavy an object is.

Z

zero

0

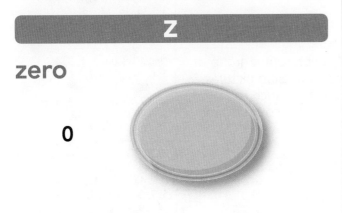

There are **zero** apples on the plate.

K.NC Number Concepts		
K.NC.1	Count by ones and by tens to 100.	Unit 1 Lessons 1, 2, 3, 4, 5, 7, 11, 17; Unit 2 Lessons 6, 8, 10, 18, 19; Unit 3 Lessons 1, 2; Unit 4 Lessons 12, 15, 16, 17; Unit 5 Lessons 2, 3, 5, 8, 10, 13, 23
K.NC.2	Count forward and backward starting at any number in a sequence; count by tens to 100 starting at any decade number.	Unit 1 Lesson 17; Unit 2 Lessons 1, 2, 6, 7, 8, 9, 10, 14, 15, 18, 19, 20; Unit 3 Lessons 1, 2, 4, 5, 7, 11, 13, 15; Unit 4 Lessons 3, 5, 7, 8, 12, 15, 16, 17, 18, 20; Unit 5 Lessons 3, 4, 5, 7, 8, 9, 10, 18, 19
K.NC.3	Read and write numbers from 0 to 31. Represent a group of objects from 0–31 by writing a numeral and using pictures, real objects, spoken words, and manipulatives such as connecting cubes. Understand that 0 means a count of no objects.	Unit 1 Lessons 1, 2, 3, 4, 5, 6, 7, 9, 11, 12, 13, 14, 15, 16, 17; Unit 2 Lessons 1, 2, 3, 4, 5, 7, 8, 9, 10, 11, 12, 14, 15, 16, 18, 19, 20; Unit 3 Lessons 1, 2, 4, 5, 6, 7, 8, 11, 12, 13, 14, 15, 16, 18, 19, 20; Unit 4 Lessons 1, 2, 3, 4, 5, 7, 8, 10, 11, 13, 16, 18, 19, 20; Unit 5 Lessons 2, 3, 4, 5, 6, 7, 8, 9, 10, 12, 13, 14, 15, 16, 17, 18, 19, 20
K.NC.4	Connect counting to the number of objects in a group; understand how numbers and quantities relate.	Unit 1 Lessons 1, 2, 3, 4, 5, 6, 7, 9, 11, 12, 13, 14, 15, 16, 17; Unit 2 Lessons 1, 2, 3, 4, 5, 7, 8, 9, 10, 11, 15, 16, 19, 20; Unit 3 Lessons 1, 2, 4, 5, 7, 11, 13, 14, 15, 18, 19, 20; Unit 4 Lessons 1, 3, 4, 5, 6, 7, 10, 12, 15, 20; Unit 5 Lessons 2, 3, 7, 9, 13, 14, 15, 16, 17, 18, 19, 23
K.NC.4.a	Count objects saying the names for numbers in correct sequence, understanding that one name for a number is paired with just one object.	Unit 1 Lessons 1, 2, 3, 4, 5, 6, 7, 9, 11, 12, 13, 14, 15, 16, 17; Unit 2 Lessons 1, 2, 3, 4, 5, 11, 15; Unit 3 Lesson 2; Unit 4 Lessons 1, 4, 10, 12; Unit 5 Lesson 5

K.NC Number Concepts

K.NC.4.b	Understand that when counting a group of objects, the last number named is the total number in the group; recognize that the total number in a group is the same no matter how the objects are arranged or the order in which they are counted.	Unit 1 Lessons 1, 2, 3, 4, 5, 6, 7, 9, 11, 12, 13, 14, 15, 16, 17; Unit 2 Lessons 1, 2, 3, 4, 5, 7, 8, 11, 15; Unit 3 Lessons 2, 8, 11, 18; Unit 4 Lessons 1, 4, 10, 12; Unit 5 Lesson 2
K.NC.4.c	When counting, understand that the next number named in sequence represents one greater than the name before it.	Unit 2 Lessons 1, 12, 14, 16, 19, 20; Unit 3 Lessons 11, 12, 13, 14; Unit 4 Lessons 4, 5, 7, 12; Unit 5 Lessons 5, 7, 9, 15, 23
K.NC.4.d	Develop understanding of ordinal numbers (first through tenth) to describe the relative position and magnitude of whole numbers.	Unit 2 Lesson 7
K.NC.5	Given 20 objects or pictures arranged in a line, array, or circle, or up through 10 scattered objects, understand that the objects or pictures can be counted to tell "How many?"; count out the number of objects named by a number 1–20.	Unit 1 Lessons 1, 2, 3, 4, 5, 6, 7, 9, 11, 12, 13, 14, 15, 16, 17; Unit 2 Lessons 1, 2, 3, 4, 5, 7, 8, 9, 12, 13, 14, 15, 16, 17, 19, 20; Unit 3 Lessons 1, 2, 3, 4, 5, 7, 8, 10, 11, 12, 13, 14, 15, 16, 17, 18, 19, 20, 21; Unit 4 Lessons 1, 2, 3, 4, 5, 7, 8, 10, 11, 12, 13, 16, 18, 19, 20; Unit 5 Lessons 2, 3, 4, 5, 6, 7, 8, 9, 10, 11, 14, 15, 16, 17, 18, 19, 20
K.NC.6	Compare two groups of objects using matching and counting strategies to identify whether the number in one group is greater than, less than, or equal to the number in the second group.	Unit 1 Lessons 9, 11, 12, 13, 16, 17; Unit 2 Lessons 7, 9, 13; Unit 3 Lessons 10, 12; Unit 4 Lessons 6, 10, 20; Unit 5 Lessons 1, 10, 14, 16, 17, 20
K.NC.7	Given two written numerals, compare numbers from 1–10.	Unit 1 Lessons 9, 15; Unit 2 Lessons 7, 9; Unit 3 Lessons 12, 14; Unit 4 Lessons 6, 10, 20; Unit 5 Lessons 16, 17, 20

K.ARO Algebraic Reasoning and Operations

K.ARO.1	Use objects, pictures, sounds (for example, tapping), mental pictures, acting out a situation, fingers, as well as expressions, equations, or explanations, to represent addition and subtraction.	Unit 1 Lessons 7, 8, 9, 11, 12, 13, 14; Unit 2 Lessons 2, 3, 4, 5, 6, 9, 10, 11, 12, 14, 15, 16, 19; Unit 3 Lessons 1, 3, 4, 5, 6, 7, 8, 11, 13, 15, 16, 17, 19, 20; Unit 4 Lessons 1, 2, 3, 4, 5, 6, 7, 8, 10, 11, 12, 13, 15, 16, 17, 18, 19, 20; Unit 5 Lessons 1, 3, 4, 5, 6, 7, 8, 9, 10, 11, 12, 13, 14, 15, 16, 17, 18, 19, 20
K.ARO.2	Add and subtract through 10; represent and solve word problems using objects or pictures or other methods that work.	Unit 1 Lessons 7, 8, 14; Unit 2 Lessons 2, 3, 5, 6, 10, 11, 12, 14, 15, 16; Unit 3 Lessons 1, 3, 4, 7, 11, 16; Unit 4 Lessons 1, 2, 3, 4, 5, 6, 7, 8, 10, 11, 12, 13, 15, 16, 17, 18, 19, 20; Unit 5 Lessons 1, 3, 4, 5, 6, 7, 8, 9, 10, 11, 12, 13, 14, 15, 16, 19
K.ARO.3	Use objects or pictures to decompose numbers into pairs in more than one way for numbers less than or equal to 10, then record the pairs by drawing pictures or writing equations, for example, $8 = 2 + 6$ and $8 = 4 + 4$.	Unit 2 Lessons 2, 20; Unit 3 Lessons 1, 3, 4, 6, 16, 17, 18; Unit 4 Lessons 2, 3, 4, 5, 7, 8, 11, 12, 13, 18, 19; Unit 5 Lessons 1, 3, 4, 5, 6, 7, 8, 9, 10, 11, 12, 13, 14, 15, 16, 18, 19
K.ARO.4	Use objects or pictures among other ways, to find a number 1 to 9 that when added to another number makes 10; record the result by drawing a picture or writing an equation.	Unit 4 Lessons 2, 4, 8, 11, 13, 18, 19; Unit 5 Lessons 2, 3, 6, 8, 11, 12, 13, 15, 18, 19
K.ARO.5	Demonstrate fluency when adding and subtracting through 5.	Unit 3 Lessons 4, 5, 6, 7, 12, 14, 18, 19; Unit 4 Lessons 3, 12, 15, 17; Unit 5 Lessons 7, 10

K.PVO Place Value and Operations

K.PVO.1	Use objects or pictures or other strategies to compose and decompose numbers into tens and ones for numbers from 11 through 19, then record the result by drawing a picture or writing an equation, for example, $10 + 5 = 15$ and $15 = 5 + 10$; understand that numbers 11–19 are made up of a group of 10 ones plus 1 through 9 other ones.	Unit 2 Lesson 10; Unit 3 Lessons 2, 3, 5, 6, 8, 13, 15, 17, 18, 19, 20; Unit 4 Lessons 3, 5, 7, 10, 12, 16, 18, 20; Unit 5 Lessons 1, 2. 3, 4, 5, 6, 7, 9, 10, 11, 15, 17, 18, 19, 20, 23

K.MDA Measurement and Data Analysis

K.MDA.1	Describe and compare attributes of everyday objects, using measurement concepts such as length, area, weight, and capacity. For an object, use measurement concepts to describe several different attributes.	Unit 5 Lessons 21, 22, 23
K.MDA.2	Directly compare and order two or three objects that have a measurement attribute in common (such as length) to determine which has more or less of the attribute; describe how they are different.	Unit 5 Lessons 21, 22, 23
K.MDA.3	Classify objects into given categories such as shape, size, color and thickness. Count the number in each category, then sort the categories into groups with the same numbers. Identify objects that do not belong to a particular group and explain the reasoning used.	Unit 1 Lesson 10; Unit 2 Lessons 13, 17; Unit 3 Lessons 10, 12, 21; Unit 4 Lessons 1, 9, 22
K.MDA.4	Explore coins (penny, nickel, dime, quarter) and begin identifying pennies and dimes.	Unit 1 Lesson 13; Unit 2 Lesson 15; Unit 3 Lesson 8; Unit 5 Lesson 8

Mathematical Standards

K.GSR Geometry and Spatial Reasoning

K.GSR.1	Describe common objects using names of geometric figures; describe relative positions of objects using terms *above, below, beside, in front of, behind, next to,* and *between*.	Unit 1 Lessons 8, 10, 18; Unit 2 Lessons 13, 17, 20: Unit 3 Lessons 10, 12, 21; Unit 4 Lessons 9, 14, 21, 22
K.GSR.2	Given geometric figures that are placed in various positions and are of different sizes, correctly name the figures.	Unit 1 Lessons 8, 10, 15, 16, 18; Unit 2 Lessons 13, 16, 17, 20: Unit 3 Lessons 9, 10, 12, 21; Unit 4 Lessons 9, 14, 21, 22
K.GSR.3	Find and identify two- and three-dimensional geometric figures; recognize that a flat figure is two-dimensional (lying in a plane) and a solid figure is three-dimensional (takes up space).	Unit 1 Lessons 8, 10, 18; Unit 2 Lesson 13; Unit 4 Lessons 9, 14, 21
K.GSR.4	Given two-and three-dimensional figures in different sizes and positions, analyze and compare them; use everyday language to describe how the figures are similar or different, how many parts they have (for example, sides or corners/vertices) among other attributes, such as lengths of sides.	Unit 1 Lessons 8, 10, 16, 18; Unit 2 Lessons 13, 17, 20; Unit 3 Lessons 10, 21; Unit 4 Lessons 9, 14, 21, 22
K.GSR.5	Create models of real-world shapes by constructing figures using blocks, sticks, clay, as well as other materials, and by drawing figures.	Unit 1 Lesson 10; Unit 3 Lesson 9; Unit 4 Lessons 9, 21
K.GSR.6	Form compound geometric figures by combining other simple figures.	Unit 3 Lesson 9; Unit 4 Lesson 21; Unit 5 Lesson 13
K.GSR.7	Identify, create, complete, and extend simple patterns using shape, color, size, number, sounds and movements. Patterns may be repeating, growing or shrinking such as ABB, ABB, ABB or •,••,•••.	Unit 1 Lessons 15, 16; Unit 2 Lessons 14, 16

MPP1

Problem Solving

Unit 1 Lessons 8, 9, 10, 15, 16, 18
Unit 2 Lessons 1, 3, 5, 6, 8, 10, 13, 14, 15, 16, 17, 20
Unit 3 Lessons 1, 4, 7, 12, 16, 21
Unit 4 Lessons 2, 3, 4, 5, 6, 9, 10, 12, 14, 15, 21, 22
Unit 5 Lessons 1, 2, 4, 5, 10, 15, 16, 21, 22, 23

MPP2

Abstract and Quantitative Reasoning

Unit 1 Lessons 6, 11, 13, 14, 15, 16, 18
Unit 2 Lessons 2, 9, 20
Unit 3 Lessons 1, 3, 4, 10, 11, 12, 14, 21
Unit 4 Lessons 1, 2, 4, 5, 6, 7, 9, 12, 16, 17, 18, 19, 22
Unit 5 Lessons 5, 7, 15, 17, 18, 20, 23

MPP3

Use and Evaluate Logical Reasoning

Unit 1 Lessons 1, 2, 3, 4, 5, 6, 8, 9, 10, 11, 12, 14, 15, 17, 18
Unit 2 Lessons 1, 2, 3, 4, 5, 6, 7, 8, 9, 10, 11, 12, 13, 14, 15, 16, 17, 18, 19, 20
Unit 3 Lessons 1, 2, 3, 4, 5, 6, 7, 8, 9, 10, 11, 12, 13, 14, 15, 16, 17, 18, 19, 20, 21
Unit 4 Lessons 1, 2, 3, 4, 5, 7, 8, 9, 10, 11, 12, 13, 14, 15, 16, 17, 18, 19, 21, 22
Unit 5 Lessons 1, 2, 3, 4, 5, 6, 7, 8, 9, 10, 11, 12, 13, 14, 15, 16, 17, 18, 19, 20, 21, 22, 23

MPP4

Mathematical Modeling

Unit 1 Lessons 1, 2, 3, 5, 8, 9, 11, 12, 13, 14, 16, 17, 18
Unit 2 Lessons 10, 11, 12, 14, 16, 19, 20
Unit 3 Lessons 1, 4, 7, 21
Unit 4 Lessons 2, 4, 6, 8, 12, 14, 20, 21, 22
Unit 5 Lessons 3, 4, 5, 6, 7, 9, 10, 12, 13, 19, 21, 23

Mathematical Processes and Practices

MPP5

Use Mathematical Tools

Unit 1 Lessons, 14, 18
Unit 2 Lessons 4, 9, 15, 19, 20
Unit 3 Lessons 5, 8, 9, 13, 20, 21
Unit 4 Lessons 5, 7, 9, 14, 20, 21, 22
Unit 5 Lessons 5, 6, 10, 19, 21, 23

MPP6

Use Precise Mathematical Language

Unit 1 Lessons 1, 2, 3, 4, 5, 6, 7, 8, 9, 10, 11, 12, 13, 14, 15, 16, 17, 18
Unit 2 Lessons 1, 2, 3, 4, 5, 6, 7, 8, 9, 10, 11, 12, 13, 14, 15, 16, 17, 18, 19, 20
Unit 3 Lessons 1, 2, 3, 4, 5, 6, 8, 9, 10, 11, 12, 13, 14, 15, 16, 17, 18, 19, 20, 21
Unit 4 Lessons 1, 2, 3, 4, 5, 7, 8, 9, 10, 11, 12, 13, 14, 15, 16, 17, 18, 19, 20, 21, 22
Unit 5 Lessons 1, 2, 3, 4, 5, 6, 7, 8, 9, 10, 11, 12, 13, 14, 15, 16, 17, 18, 19, 20, 21, 22, 23

MPP7

See Structure

Unit 1 Lessons 1, 4, 5, 6, 7, 8, 9, 10, 13, 15, 16, 17, 18
Unit 2 Lessons 2, 3, 4, 5, 7, 8, 12, 13, 14, 15, 16, 17, 20
Unit 3 Lessons 2, 5, 6, 7, 8, 9, 10, 11, 15, 16, 17, 21
Unit 4 Lessons 1, 2, 4, 5, 6, 7, 8, 9, 11, 12, 13, 14, 15, 16, 20, 21, 22
Unit 5 Lessons 3, 6, 7, 8, 9, 11, 13, 14, 15, 17, 18, 20, 23

MPP8

Generalize

Unit 1 Lessons 4, 7, 10, 11, 14, 15, 16, 17, 18
Unit 2 Lessons 14, 16, 19, 20
Unit 3 Lessons 4, 5, 6, 7, 8, 9, 10, 12, 13, 14, 15, 17, 18, 19, 20, 21
Unit 4 Lessons 5, 6, 7, 9, 13, 15, 22
Unit 5 Lessons 15, 16, 17, 18, 20, 23

A

Add, 150

Addition. *See also* **Algebra.**
with 5-counter strips, 105–106
with 5-groups, 73–74, 77
equations, 99–100, 150, 156, 159,
   186, 257–258, 263–264, 270–271,
   282, 326, 334, 350, 356
partner equations, 273–274
partners. *See* Partners.
plus (+) tile, 86
stories, 45–46, 82
teen numbers and, 299

Algebra
addition
   both addends unknown, 225–226,
      237–238, 253, 260, 326,
      343–347, 349
   equations, 147–148, 156, 160,
      161, 188, 192, 206, 225–226,
      229–233, 237–238, 253,
      257–258, 260, 263–264, 270,
      271, 273–274, 277, 282,
      289–290, 299–300, 307–309,
      311–312, 319–323, 326, 328,
      336, 345–346, 350, 365, 379
   one addend unknown, 73–74,
      161, 241–242, 308, 319–323,
      328, 351, 361, 365
   partners, 147–148, 195, 203,
      225–226, 273, 277, 325, 333,
      343–347, 349
   represent problems, 83, 229
   subtraction and, 45–46, 83, 97
subtraction
   addition and, 45–46, 83, 97
   equations, 150, 156, 160, 188,
      192, 206, 230, 258, 264, 272,
      278, 289–290, 311–312, 326,
      327, 335, 363–364, 366, 380

represent problems, 230, 318
symbols
   equal (=), 85, 187, 190, 191, 335,
      357
   minus (−), 72, 86
   not equal (≠), 86, 187, 191, 335
   plus (+), 71, 85

Alike, 187

Area, 373
drawing rectangles to match, 374

Assessment
Fluency Check, 233–234, 247–248,
   289–290, 311–312, 353–354,
   379–380
Formative Assessment
   Performance Task, 65–66,
      135–136, 215–216, 295–296,
      385–386
   Unit Review/Test, 61–64,
      131–134, 211–214, 291–294,
      381–384
Strategy Check, 265–266, 327–328

At Home Number Cards, 153–154

B

Behind, 210. *See also* **Geometry.**

Below, 210. *See also* **Geometry.**

Beside, 210

Between, 210

C

Capacity, 376

Cent, 41. *See also* **Money.**
identifying number of, 42

Cent sign (¢), 41

Index

Equal sign (=)
and not equal (≠) tile, 86
tile, 86

Equal to (=), 185, 335

Equations, 230
addition, 99–100, 150, 159,
257–258, 263, 264, 270–271, 282,
326, 334, 350, 356
partner, 273–274, 277
subtraction, 150, 159, 230, 258,
272, 278, 326, 335, 348, 356,
363–364, 366
teen equation cards, 227
teen numbers, 229–230, 309
teen partners, 365

F

Faces
of cube, 261
on different shapes, 283

**Family letter, 1–2, 9–10, 35–36,
67–68, 137–138, 145–146, 151–152,
157–158, 201–202, 217–218,
235–236, 255–256, 297–298,
305–306, 367–368**

Fewer, 33–34. See also Compare.

Fifteen
tens in, 339
writing, 162, 192

Five
groups of, 16, 18, 50
partners, 325
writing, 51, 58, 70, 87

Five-Counter Strips, 77, 79–80
and addition, 105–106, 189

Flat shapes, 250. See also Geometry.

Fluency
Check, 233–234, 247–248, 289–290,
311–312, 353–354, 379–380
Path to Fluency, 150, 158, 160, 162,
186, 192, 204, 206, 230, 258, 264,
270, 271–272, 274, 282, 326, 334,
348, 356, 363–364, 366

Four
groups of, 15, 18, 50
writing, 43, 58, 70

Fourteen
tens in, 339
writing, 159

G

**Geometry. See also Cone; Cube;
Cylinder; Hexagon; Rectangle;
Sphere; Square; Triangle.**
attributes, 250, 261
corners, 249, 260
faces, 261, 283
sides, 59–60, 104, 175
in environment, 59, 104, 130, 287
that roll/don't roll, 283
that stack/don't stack, 283
three-dimensional shapes
attributes of, 250, 283
compare with two-dimensional,
250, 266
compose, 284–285
cone, 250, 262, 283, 288
cube, 250, 261–262, 266, 267, 283,
288
cylinder, 250, 262, 283, 287–288
position (above, behind, below,
in front), 262
solid, 250, 266
sort, 250, 283

Index

Index

groups of, 75–76, 143, 144, 155
and ones, 361–362
partners, 225–226, 231–232, 243,
303, 345, 346, 347
partners of, with 5-groups, 253
in teen numbers, 337, 343–344
writing, 109–110

Ten-Counter Strips, 141
and teen numbers, 275, 279

Ten-Sticks
and circles, 316

Thirteen
tens in, 339
writing, 159

Three
groups of, 12, 13, 18, 50
writing, 38, 40, 58, 70

Tiny Tumblers. *See* **Math Mountains.**

Triangle. *See also* **Geometry.**
drawing, 109
identifying, 103, 123–124, 129–130

Twelve
tens in, 339
writing, 156

Twenty
writing, 206

Two
groups of, 11, 14, 18, 50
writing, 37, 58, 70, 87

W

Weight, 375

Writing Numbers
37–38, 40, 43, 51, 56, 58, 70, 81–82,
87–88, 91, 93–94, 95–96, 98,
109–110, 125–126, 127–128, 140,
149, 156, 159, 162, 192, 204, 206,
245

Z

Zero
writing, 56, 70

© Houghton Mifflin Harcourt Publishing Company

Be an Illustrator

Illustrator: Josh Brill

Did you ever try to use shapes to draw animals like the seahorse on the cover?

Over the last 10 years Josh has been using geometric shapes to design his animals. His aim is to keep the animal drawings simple and use color to make them appealing.

Add some color to the seahorse Josh drew. Then try drawing a cat or dog or some other animal using the shapes below.

Shape Toolbox